ZLDUS4E5SH   #25
                              ──
                              RD

Brady & Lawless's
FAVORITE BOOKSTORES

Brady & Lawless's
FAVORITE
BOOKSTORES

Frank Brady and Joann Lawless

Illustrations by Carl Pugliese

SHEED ANDREWS AND McMEEL, INC.
Subsidiary of Universal Press Syndicate
KANSAS CITY

Library of Congress Cataloging in Publication Data

Brady, Frank.
    Brady & Lawless's Favorite bookstores.

    Includes index.
    1. Booksellers and bookselling—United States—
Directories. I. Lawless, Joann A., 1949–
joint author. II. Title. III. Title: Favorite
bookstores.
Z475.B75   658.8'09'0705730973   78-9839
ISBN 0-8362-7902-6

For a book is not the end of a voyage,
but the beginning.

Holbrook Jackson

Preface

Almost everyone who reads has, at some point, been seduced by the charm of a good bookstore. A bookstore experience can sometimes be memorable: browsing on a lazy or lonely afternoon, one may delight in finding—and establishing a friendship with—a long sought-after volume of one's favorite author. There is also the serendipitous experience of discovering a book—without knowing that one even existed—concerning a subject that one has been eager to explore. But bookstores are often much more than merely shops where books are unearthed, bought, and sold—they have a life of their own. Consider the eccentric personality of a shop such as the Gotham Book Mart (which we describe in the New York listings), for years a belletristic oasis in the jungle of mid-town Manhattan. Its former owner, Frances Stellof, a grade-school dropout but a consummate lover of books, charmed and inspired many of the greatest American writers of the past generation. Although much of the stock of poetry and "little" magazines has been sold recently, the store still contains one of the city's—if not the country's—best collections of hard-to-get books on theater and film.

Books are concepts, men's thoughts housed in receptacles of paper, ink, and binding for hundreds, possibly thousands, of years to come. Bookstores are an important part of our literary culture. They have also served, since the Renaissance, as social and historical centers—quiet marketplaces for ideas. Good bookstores are essential to authors and publishers as well as to readers and browsers; they reflect the variety and vitality of the intellectual and artistic life of the cities and countries they serve.

The pleasures of reading books are often enhanced by the act of buying them, and by having them there on one's shelves always at the ready, for knowledge, stimulation, and companionship. The purchase of books is especially rewarding if one's neighborhood store features a coffeepot, a knowledgeable and possibly engaging owner, displays of new titles by local and internationally known authors, and a coterie of book-loving friends and browsers. Bookstores are among the few places where intimate exchange and communication still occur: a discussion with a fellow customer, a remark by an interested sales clerk, two customers buying the same book at the same time exchanging glances of interest and rapport. Recently, at a New York bookstore, for example, a friend bent down for a thin volume of poetry, was startled by a nearby browser, and stood up to stare at the writer whose picture was on the back cover. And one author told us of the excitement of watching a browser pick the author's latest book, page through it carefully, put it down again, come back to it, and finally take it to the cash register.

Favorite Bookstores is a guidebook to a number of stores throughout the United States and Canada which we have selected by no method other than visiting them or browsing in their aisles, talking to their owners and sometimes to their customers, reading about them, and, finally, *enjoying* them. Undoubtedly, we have included many, but certainly not all, or even most, of the "best" bookstores in America: we did not attempt to be comprehensive. We simply set out to describe those stores that have special meaning to us, and those that most other booklovers might find equally interesting and friendly. We have also had to limit the scope of the book and thus were unable to include descriptions of some of the great bookstores—other than in the U.S. and Canada—throughout the world, such as Blackwell's and Foyle's in England, Shakespeare & Co. and La Hune in Paris, Kinokuniya in Tokyo, Alemar's in Manila, Steinmatsky's in Israel, and Libreria Feltrinelli in Italy, all of which, along with many others, will be described in a future international edition of *Favorite*

Bookstores.

If we have failed to mention anyone's favorite store—and we are certain we have—a store that has special character, gives extraordinary service, has an unforgettable owner, is historically important in the life of literature, or is just a comfortable, well-stocked shop that carries outstanding books, then we suggest that our readers write to us, in care of the publisher, and perhaps we will be able to visit the store and include a description of it in future editions of *Favorite Bookstores*.

Please note that if you are planning a bookstore trip, a journey from city to city to visit the stores listed in *Favorite Bookstores*, you might want to write or call in advance to be certain of the days and hours they are open. Although we have attempted to include the most accurate and up-to-date information possible, hours and days of bookstores have a tendency to change, especially in smaller stores. Also bear in mind that almost all stores have extended hours and are open extra days during the year-end holiday season.

We hope that *Favorite Bookstores* will serve as a guidebook for the traveler who loves to browse, as a reference book for those who do their shopping and seeking of books by mail, and as an informal history of the contemporary American bookstore. If you do visit a new store on the strength of this book, please give our regards.

Finally, we would like to thank Maxine Brady and Harold and Jean Lawless for their help.

Alabama

HAUNTED BOOK SHOP

MOBILE ALABAMA

Lest you think that this bookstore is something out of a Charles Addams cartoon and carries only books concerning ghouls, monsters, and hobgoblins, the word "haunted" applies here to something else: the shop, according to the owner, Mrs. Cameron Plummer, is "haunted by the ghosts of all great literature." The building that the store occupies, however, might, indeed, have some ghostly connotations. It is the oldest building in Mobile, built in 1819. The city of Mobile, founded in 1711, is the oldest on the Gulf Coast. A carriage drive, once used by the Southern aristocracy, runs right through the middle of the house, to a courtyard with two buildings in back, one of which was once slave quarters.

In addition to atmosphere, the Haunted Book Shop has a fine selection of books consisting of new and used general titles, with a strong emphasis on Southern material. It also has a good selection of children's books and technical books, and carries maps, original art work, and old bottles.

In a city with few good general bookshops, the Haunted Book Shop (founded thirty-five years ago) was a pioneer. It is still one of the best stores in the area.

150 Government St., Mobile, Alabama 36602; Tel. 205-432-6606. Hours: Monday–Friday, 10:00 A.M.–5:00 P.M.; Saturday, 10:00 A.M.–4:00 P.M.

Alaska

OLD HARBOR BOOKS   **SITKA**
                                                       ALASKA

In the eighteenth century, the picturesque town of Sitka, then known as New Archangel, located on Baranof Island, about one hundred miles southwest of Juneau and eight, hundred miles north of Seattle, Washington, was the seat of the Russian Territorial Government. After the purchase of Alaska by the United States in 1867, Sitka became the capital of the territory and remained so until 1906. Today, Sitka is a prospering but small town of eight thousand people; it is dominated by a local paper mill and a thriving fishing industry. Despite the fact that Baranof Island is often ice-locked for long stretches of time and that, at best, it is only accessible by air or sea, three adventurous couples, Lee and Linda Schmidt, Chuck and Alice Johnstone, and Mary and Don Muller, decided the populace of Sitka and the many tourists who visit the island throughout the year needed a good, well-stocked bookstore. In March of 1976, Old Harbor Books was born.

The shop specializes in and carries a fairly large selection of new and out-of-print books on "Alaskana," although it is primarily a general service store with books of all kinds: new, hard, paperback, fiction, and nonfiction. The atmosphere of the store is relaxed and rustic. Wood is everywhere and the shelves are all hand-made from logs that have washed up on the nearby beach. A small office at the back of the store has been donated to and is used by a representative of the Southeast Alaska Conservation Council. Old Harbor Books serves as a center for conservation, and issues current information on outdoor activities of the island to hikers and to anyone else who

2

is interested. The store personnel have already become involved in some controversial conservation issues of a public nature and feel that it is a bookseller's place to make a stand on such issues, if necessary.

Tourists use the shop as a place to gather information about the history, culture, and activities of Sitka. Perhaps influenced by the Russian architecture (Old Harbor Books is right across the street from a magnificent Russian Orthodox Church), tourists often become confused over Sitka's Russian heritage and have asked such questions of the bookstore staff as: Do you ever use American money? or, Where can I buy Russian stamps?

Everyone who works in Old Harbor Books (there is a staff of three at any given time) attempts to keep *au courant* of what is being published and what books will be of interest to their clientele. As one of the owners stated: "We believe that a bookseller should be *widely* read and this includes reading in areas where we have no strong interest: it requires a good deal of effort on our parts."

233 Lincoln Street, Box 1827, Sitka, Alaska 99835; Tel: 907-747-8808; Hours: Monday–Saturday, 9:00 A.M–6:00 P.M.

Arizona

THE BOOK MARK

**TUCSON
ARIZONA**

In this large, long, and relaxed bookstore, there are, out of 100,000 new books in stock, close to 5,000 titles on Western Americana and Indians alone, specially sectioned to be easy to find. It's possible to discover here a biography of Billy the Kid or Jesse James; an enormous volume called *The Filming of the West*; a book on the varieties of cactus; an intimate memoir of an old Navajo; the story of Wounded Knee.

Although the Book Mark is famous for its plentiful stock of books on the West, it considers itself the most "complete" bookstore in Arizona, and, in addition to hardbacks of all categories, it carries paperbacks of fiction and nonfiction, as well as maps and posters.

Occasionally, the Book Mark sponsors a local poet in a reading from his works, or invites a traveling author to stop by for an autographing party in his honor. The store's main thrust is service to its customers, however. Owner Edward Eggers and his capable staff of six are known for their patience and courtesy in giving customers all the help they may require in finding the one book that will suit their needs and interests. Friendliness and casual efficiency pervade the atmosphere of the store, and the staff works by the credo of Arthur Chapman:

> Out where the handclasp's a little stronger,
> Out where the smile dwells a little longer,
> That's where the West begins.

4765 East Speedway, Tucson, Arizona 85712; Tel. 602-881-6350. Hours: Monday–Friday, 9:00 A.M.–6:00 P.M.; Saturday, 9:00 A.M.– 5:00 P.M.

4

Arkansas

PUBLISHERS BOOKSHOP, INC.

LITTLE ROCK ARKANSAS

A few years ago Publishers Bookshop, in a continuing effort to raise the literary level of its community, decided to give away free copies of the complete works of Shakespeare. All any person interested in acquiring the book needed to do was summarize three of Shakespeare's plays, and the full purchase price of the book (four dollars, plus twelve cents tax) would be refunded. Anyone who could not afford the expenditure in the first place could have the book outright if he signed an agreement stating that he would provide the store with the three summaries. Additionally, for those who could not afford to get to the bookshop, the book would be delivered or mailed to the home, again, free of charge. Within a short time after the announcement of the unique reading program was made, the store was besieged by people interested in the offer. Eventually, some eighty-four books were delivered in this manner and only one person who had promised to do the play summaries failed to write them. Although the store was heartened by the response and had every intention of continuing the practice of free dissemination of Shakespeare's works, the hobgoblin of bureaucracy, in the guise of the tax department of the Department of Finance and Administration of the state of Arkansas, decided that the 3 percent sales/use tax had to be paid by the store for the books that had been distributed free. The store owner, James W. Bell, became disgusted with the enforced governmental levy and discontinued the program, choosing to work in nonprofit channels that would not be taxed. The state of Arkansas apparently remains unaware of the potentiality of the contribution that the Publishers Bookshop was making to its citizens.

Mr. Bell is clear about the role of his bookstore: "The scores on the standard achievement tests for high school students in Pulaski County [Arkansas] are now significantly higher than the national average. We like to think that this is because of our store in part. We work with both public and private schools, we support literary publications and encourage student participation. We also work with the local publisher to encourage would-be authors and already established authors."

The Publishers Bookshop consists of two shops, a very large store that carries general books and a smaller store that carries technical books of all kinds. Although the staff will order books for customers and perform other services, the shop exists primarily to provide maximum access to the largest number of books possible for the people in central Arkansas. Indeed, the store has one of the widest selections of books between St. Louis and Dallas, and people come from out of the state just to buy books at the Publishers Bookshop. In addition to general and technical books, the shop carries the largest selection of black literature and feminist literature in Little Rock. Mr. Bell sums up his feeling about his store: "Some people describe us as a 'carriage trade' bookstore. This is a wrong image. With our technical and professional books and our huge supply of other books we really are a bookstore for intellectuals. That's how we like to be known, in any event."

7509 Cantrell Road (general), Little Rock, Arkansas 72207; Tel. 501-664-6941. Hours: Monday–Friday, 10:00 A.M.–7:00 P.M.; Saturday, 10:00 A.M.–6:00 P.M.
104 Tanglewood Shopping Center (technical), Little Rock, Arkansas 72207; Tel. 501-664-6956. Hours: Monday–Friday, 10:00 A.M.–6:00 P.M.; Saturday, 10:00 A.M.–3:00 P.M.

California

BOOKS UNLIMITED CO-OP

BERKELEY CALIFORNIA

There are more than sixty bookstores in Berkeley, California, a town that has a close relationship to one of the great educational institutions, the University of California, and, as a consequence, one of the most erudite communities in America. Books Unlimited, a three-store chain of general bookstores (new, hardcover, and paperbound books), in many ways represents the spirit of Berkeley: fiercely independent, highly intellectual, and socially aware.

BU, as it's affectionately known by just about everyone, has one of the most unusual structures of any bookstore in the U.S. It is a cooperative corporation, owned by some five thousand members who own a minimum of ten dollars in shares and who receive certain benefits for their support: patronage refunds on purchases; free mailing of any book to a domestic address; a subscription to *Pinecones*, a periodic newsletter which discusses newsworthy books, gives reviews, and reports current activities of the co-op. But aside from these membership privileges, perhaps the most valuable asset of membership in Books Unlimited is the opportunity it gives its members to participate in the life of the organization. The group does quite a bit more than just sell books: BU leaders work with educators, librarians, and teachers to help them gain a better understanding of the importance of books. Other activities include book fairs, lending books to organizations for displays, sponsoring workshops, and furnishing resource people for events in the community. If a parent is concerned about the reading level of his or her child, bookstore personnel will not only spend as much time as is necessary helping the parent (and the child) to find a book, but will actually serve as counselors in guiding the child to appropriate and useful books.

Aside from the social energy expressed in many ways, BU has also attempted to have an effect on bookselling itself. The managers of the stores and the staff of the co-op serve and work with regional and national bookselling associations, taking the role of consumer advocates, and have fought over such issues as pricing, quality control, copyrights, advertising, and the rights of authors. They also seem to work constantly to alert the public against censorship efforts by various groups and against any kind of legislation that will interfere with the freedom to read. So astute are they in understanding what the public wants to read that they also act as counsel to aspiring writers, editors, and publishers, giving them a perspective on current trends and changing patterns in reading tastes.

With all its social activity and community consciousness, it would seem that Books Unlimited could have little time to actually sell books. Untrue. All of the stores are always crowded; people keep coming back—they frequent BU as a gathering place. They also are often known to buy a book—or two—or three.

1975 Shattuck Avenue (main store), Berkeley, California; Tel. 415-845-6288. Hours: Monday–Friday, 9:00 A.M.–7:00 P.M.; Saturday, 9:00 A.M.–6:00 P.M.; Sunday 1:00 P.M.–5:00 P.M.

MOE'S BOOKS   BERKELEY CALIFORNIA

Fact: there are over 200,000 books in this store at any given time. Fact: there are extensive collections of art books, illustrated children's books, first editions, and scholarly books.

Fact: it is possible to pick up a used copy of *Siddhartha* for as little as fifty cents or the original first edition of *The Wizard of Oz* for six hundred dollars. And yet, despite all of the above, probably the most important reason why Moe's is one of the great bookstores in the United States is its generous trade policy, one of the most liberal in the country for a major bookstore. New and used books and records are bought, sold, and swapped at Moe's, on the following basis: for quality paperbacks, 30 percent of the cover price in cash or 50 percent in trade (credit which can be applied to future purchases at Moe's); for pocketbooks in good condition, 20 percent of the cover price in cash or 40 percent in trade; for hardcover books, individual offers and quotations that are quite simply the highest in the state of California. Most stores will give only 30 percent in trade, for example, for quality paperbacks. Moe's will also give 50 percent of the retail price for records and 75 percent in trade for clean used records. This liberal policy has enabled many students from the University of California— located down the block from Moe's—to trade in their books from term to term, acquiring the texts that they need for the next semester or some much-needed cash to see them through a difficult time—sometimes a combination of both.

The trade policy—in addition to excellent buying and precise shelving—also accounts for a phenomenal turnover of stock. Each week seems to bring in enormous quantities of books that weren't on the shelves the week before. Moe's also carries records, cards, maps, and some original prints; Visa and Master Charge are accepted. The store occasionally issues a specialized catalog.

A stop at Moe's is virtually *de rigueur* during a visit to Berkeley. Although the store is mostly frequented by students and faculty members from the university, there seems to be an endless stream of Bay Area artists and writers coming into the store at all times, and recently Lina Wertmüller browsed the aisles of Moe's at approximately the same time Kareem Abdul-

9

Jabbar was searching for a book.

The owner of Moe's, Morris Moskowitz—who says business has increased 900 percent since he opened in 1962—has become almost a legendary figure in Berkeley, presiding over his store with a Churchillian cigar, dispensing knowledge and prices of books, and operating his store like a literary general. The cigar might give him trouble in the future, however. A tough antismoking ordinance, which bans smoking in all retail stores, was recently passed in California. Moe says he has no intention of giving up smoking in his own store. He adds, philosophically: "It is possible for someone to arrest me in my own store. I wonder if the city council knows about a recent study made on a controlled group of ten humans that demonstrated that half again the usual degree of righteousness produces as many cancer cells as you would get from having ten thousand rats smoking human cigars ten hours a day for two years. The skeptics' premise that you can't solve one problem without creating a new one applies perfectly here."

Meanwhile, Moe continues to sell. A history of Japanese temples in sixteen volumes? The complete plays of Eugene O'Neill? A slightly used copy of Toscanini conducting Beethoven's Ninth?

2476 Telegraph Avenue, Berkeley, California 94704; Tel. 415-849-2087. Hours: Monday–Sunday, 10:00 A.M.–11:00 P.M.

CODY'S BOOKS   BERKELEY
CALIFORNIA

The people who frequent Cody's Books, one of the finest general bookstores in California, seem to come from a myriad of occupations and professions. Freshmen browse next to seasoned professors, housewives from the Berkeley Hills line up to buy books behind aging hippies from Telegraph Avenue, radicals buying a copy of *Coma* exchange a few words with doctors picking up a copy of the quotations of Chairman Mao. The store is also host to the many authors who live in the Bay Area, from Herbert Gold to Ishmael Reed. Perhaps the most notable author ever to shop at Cody's was Aldous Huxley. "He was like me," says Fred Cody, who, with his wife, Pat, owned the shop for over twenty years. "He couldn't look at anything in print and not read it. One day he bought some books and paid for them with a twenty-dollar traveler's check. That check, with its two signatures, signed by a man I respected so much, was the kind of thing a bookseller likes to frame and display right over the front counter. But I had four kids to feed and I was a struggling young bookseller and so, after much vacillation, I cashed it for groceries."

Recently, the Codys sold the shop, and others now operate it. Their memory and the impact that they had on bookselling in Berkeley can still be felt, however.

People who know the Codys love to relate stories about them. There was the time that the store was closed for a week—during the Berkeley riots—after the police fired tear-gas cannisters through the front window. Once they asked a relatively unknown author to appear for what would be a "small autographing session," only to have sixty students, feeling no pain, show up to harangue Carlos Castaneda for not writing about LSD. And when a clerk in San Francisco was arrested for selling Allen Ginsberg's *Howl*, Cody packed his front window with hundreds of copies as a protest. The Berkeley police? They smiled about it.

During a booksellers' convention in the early 1970s, Cody turned a panel discussion into an encounter-psychodrama about students, rebellion, and drugs and had half the audience on its feet screaming, "What has this to do with selling books!" while the other half stood up shouting, "Everything!"

When the Codys opened their first shop, the place was referred to as a "glorified phone booth"; it had no heat, no

11

bathroom, and no office. Fred Cody wore his thermal underwear all year long. There was no stockroom, so when they ran out of space, books were simply displayed on the floor. Later they moved to a prime location in Berkeley.

Cody's became the center of everything, much to Fred's delight. The riots. Viet Nam. Student strikes. Eldridge Cleaver. Kent State. Third World. Drugs. Jesus freaks. The marches always began on campus and finished in a holocaust of tear gas and night sticks, right in front of Cody's.

Even though the Codys were a focal point of protest, they didn't start all the problems. They simply felt that a bookseller's job is to point the way. And you can't point the way to anything unless you're involved and in the forefront. Today, Cody looks back on it all and says, "It was good business. The audience thrived on it and we sold a lot of books. But we also paid our dues."

Fred is also a writer. He has already completed one book, *Haunted Homes* (Doubleday), and now aspires to write a book about bookselling. "It won't be a manual like the *American Booksellers Association Handbook*," he says, "but, well—something different."

2454 Telegraph Avenue, Berkeley, California 94704; Tel. 415-845-7852. Hours: Monday–Friday, 10:00 A.M.–10:45 P.M.; Saturday, 10:15 A.M.–9:45 P.M.; Sunday, 12:00 Noon–6:00 P.M.

HUNTER'S BOOKS   BEVERLY HILLS CALIFORNIA

Recently, someone spotted Paul Newman staring into the window of Hunter's Books. He has probably shopped there many times. Inside, the store sometimes takes on the ambience of a convention of entertainment industry personalities: Sidney Sheldon, Johnny Carson, Truman Capote, Francis

Hunter's Books, Beverly Hills, California

Ford Coppola, Ray Bradbury, Joan Didion, Cary Grant, and Neil Simon all shop there, and Hunter's has the fastest-selling fiction table in the West. As one pundit explained: all the screenwriters, actors, producers, and directors in Hollywood are looking for that one multi-million-dollar movie property and use Hunter's as their principal source of literary supply.

Hunter's is huge. It stocks over eighty thousand new books and employs thirty-five people to service its customers. The store specializes in art, travel, and fiction and also has an extensive children's department. The store will accept Visa credit cards and Master Charge.

Located on the corner at Rodeo Drive, which is fast becoming one of the most fashionable shopping streets in the world, Hunter's, according to its owner, Lewis Lengfeld, resides comfortably alongside such blue-chip neighbors as Vidal Sassoon, Hermès, Gucci, and Courrèges. Incidentally, Joseph Thorndike's *The Very Rich*, published in 1976, was one of the store's most popular sellers.

463 N. Rodeo Drive, Beverly Hills, California 90210; Tel. 213-274-7301. Hours: Monday–Saturday, 9:30 A.M.–6:00 P.M.

THE MAGIC FISHBONE   CARMEL CALIFORNIA

In the realm of children's literature, California seems more advanced than other areas of the country. While some states have one or two children's bookstores, California boasts eight, and the Magic Fishbone, founded in 1963, is the oldest, possibly the best.

Every book in the store is carefully selected for its excellence in story, literary form, and artistic format by the owner, Martha Bruggeman Legg, who has ten years' experience as an elementary school teacher and who is known nationwide for her professionalism in the field of children's literature. "I want to win young readers over to the love of books," she says. And everything she does in the store is dedicated to that aim. The stock of fifteen thousand books—the largest selection of children's books in the country—includes a variety of interesting titles: poetry, fantasy, folklore, mythology, historical fiction, nonfiction, and professional material in the study of children's literature. In between the giving of literary advice and the dispensing of books, Martha finds time to look up a line from a forgotten poem, conduct autograph parties, have regular teas, mount special exhibits, organize parent discussion groups and classes in children's literature, give talks to school groups, and spend as much time as possible with mothers of preschool children, helping them to know what books are right for their about-to-read children.

"Reading is the most human tool to life," says Martha, "and books are the most influential experience in a child's life. They can inspire or degrade it. If we don't build readers from the nursery up, we will be left without readers in adult life." The Magic Fishbone attempts to uplift. Its motto, a quote from Walter de la Mare, is an indication of how Martha sees her goal: "Only the rarest kind of best in anything can be good enough for the young."

Mission and 7th, P.O. Box 3473, Carmel, California 93921; Tel. 408-624-4444. Hours: Monday–Saturday, 10:00 A.M.–5:30 P.M.

PICKWICK BOOKS   HOLLYWOOD
CALIFORNIA

Located a few blocks from Grauman's Chinese Theater, Pickwick is the bookshop where movie stars rub elbows with the reading public, and where gossip columnists stop off every day to learn what's going on in Hollywood. The first of sixteen stores, it was founded by Louis Epstein in 1938. Pickwick is largely responsible for making Los Angeles the second largest book market in the United States. It sells new and remaindered hardcover and paperback books. Nathanael West, Robert Benchley, and the F. Scott Fitzgeralds did their buying there, as did Charles Laughton, who bought armloads of books, and Bing Crosby, who used to buy hundreds of books to send to his friends.

Once, in the 1930s, when Epstein was still selling used books, he received a call from Paramount Studios asking to rent twenty thousand books (half his stock) for a film, *No Man of Her Own* (with Carole Lombard playing a librarian and Clark Gable, a gambler). For the scenes in the library, Paramount didn't have enough books on hand. They offered to send a crew at 7:00 A.M. with six-wheeled trucks and trailers to cart them off. There was one catch—Epstein was in the middle of several pending rare book deals, expecting customers to drop by at any time, and he needed to close the sales. The solution: Epstein was given permission to enter the soundstage with a customer and make a sale any time except during the actual shooting. Pickwick is probably the only bookstore in history to relocate and do business on a movie set.

Perhaps the best description of the history and operation of the Pickwick has been given, recently, by Epstein in an article in the *Los Angeles Times*, from which the following is extracted:

The Pickwick Bookshop—subtitled "The Big Bookshop"—opened its doors at 6743 Hollywood Blvd. in May of 1938. We were lucky to have the help of a bright young man named Edwin F. Stackhouse, who had learned the book business at Leary's Book Store of Philadelphia. Over the years, after we closed the 8th St. location and combined our inventory at the Hollywood store, Ed Stackhouse took charge of buying used books while I concentrated on our growing stock of new books.

Pickwick got into the new book business reluctantly. We started receiving requests for new books, and we finally decided to stock a few best-sellers. Our first inventory of new books consisted of five copies of *The Grapes of Wrath*. Although Hollywood had plenty of other new book stores, our new book inventory began to take up more than half of our space.

The big shift to new books came when World War II called Ed Stackhouse away from his civilian duties. When Ed returned from the wars, the ground floor of Pickwick was given over to new books. And a new phenomenon in the publishing business—remainder books—began pushing the used books out of the upstairs old-book department. We tried to stay in the used book business by selling them through the Argonaut on 6th St.—a shop that I owned and my brother, Ben, operated—but Ben's health made it impossible. We finally gave all of our used books to UCLA. And to this day, I am called a traitor by used book sellers for having given up that portion of our business.

In the fall of 1952, my older son, Aaron, entered the business. I have always said that Aaron had the hardest job in the world—working with his father. It wasn't long after Aaron came in that he developed an advertising and publicity policy that was largely responsible for the growth of our business, especially after we started our *branches*. Nick Clemente, who was brought in by Aaron as his assistant, is now the advertising manager for the entire *B. Dalton-Pickwick chain of over 220 bookstores*.

We had some great bookmen working with us over the years. In addition to Ed Stackhouse, of course, there were Herman Mann and "Sven" Svenseid—both now deceased—and Lloyd Harkema, who recently retired. Three others are still with the main store—Guy Thompson, Ben Latting (who manages the store), and Eliot Leonard (who came to us from the Harvard Coop, and who is now manager of the entire Western region of the chain).

The endless tales that I could tell about the people I encountered in the book business would fill many times the space allotted to me. Jimmy Cagney, for instance, liked to drop by the 8th St. bookstore and chat with me in Yiddish. Charlie Chaplin used to complain that the used books were marked too high—but he always seemed to find one that was worth the price. Marlene Dietrich, one of our most regular browsers, was once mistaken for a clerk by another customer—and she played the whole scene from beginning to end. Finally, one of our clerks told the customer: "You had the highest-priced book clerk in the world waiting on you."

We often saw the leading lights of Southern California's intellectual colony—Stravinsky and Feuchtwanger and Mann and Brecht, Faulkner and Fitzgerald and Dreiser and Huxley. Brecht, I recall, was strapped for money during his stay in Hollywood, and he called me to his apartment above Sunset to buy some of his books. William Faulkner lived around the corner, and he would stop by the Pickwick several times a week to buy books for himself or to send to his daughter in Oxford, Mississippi. He was very particular about capitalizing "Mississippi," pointing out repeatedly that there are towns called Oxford in every state of the Union. And I recall Aldous Huxley's first visit to our 8th St. shop in search of a used Bible. I remember them all—the actors, the writers, the directors, the photographers, the artists, the scholars, the real and the phony.

It has been eight years since I sold the Pickwick Bookshop, and four years since I retired. But in retirement I have regressed to acting just like a used book man, haunting the thrift shops and old bookstores, collecting used books just as I did fifty years ago. And what's especially gratifying is again meeting the old friends that I've made along the way.

Elia Kazan once told me that the Pickwick helped him through one of the worst periods of his life. He said he would have gone mad or committed suicide if there hadn't been a place where he could browse through old books and pick one up to read, a place where a friendly face would help him find what he'd been looking for.

When I think of Elia Kazan's words, I realize what the book trade has meant to me. We worked hard, we helped people, we created, we enjoyed what we did, success crowned our efforts, and we think that we left a good name.

6743 Hollywood Blvd., Hollywood, California 90028; Tel. 213-469-8191. Hours: Sunday–Thursday, 9:30 A.M.–10:00 P.M.; Friday and Saturday, 9:30 A.M.–11:00 P.M.

BODHI TREE BOOKSTORE　　LOS ANGELES CALIFORNIA

The sacred bodhi is the fig tree under which Buddha is said to have sat while he attained perfect wisdom. One of these trees is planted next to every temple in Ceylon, and each is supposed to be derived from Buddha's original tree, giving it

Bodhi Tree Bookstore, Los Angeles, California

spiritual meaning. In more recent times, the term *Bodhi* has come to signify the path to enlightenment. The Bodhi Tree Bookstore, therefore, is a shop that carries books and other items that attempt to help people understand themselves and the cosmos and to guide them in their participation in the process of self-development and self-knowledge.

The Bodhi Tree specializes in books on the religions and philosophies of the world. It sells both hardback and paperbound books, new and used, fiction and nonfiction, in an atmosphere that is soft and soothing. A visitor can sit and read, drink tea (black, green, or herbal, compliments of the store), listen to conversations among customers and present-day vagabonding messiahs, or enjoy the selections of classical and folk records of music from around the world. In addition to selling books, the shop acts as an information center covering related organizations, publications, lectures, and special events. It also stocks and sells an extensive selection of incense, herbs and teas (over eighty varieties), children's toys (mostly handcrafted), cards, some "New Age" jewelry, tarot cards, pendulums, and crystal balls. The shelves are handcrafted of naturally finished redwood. The floors are golden oak, with large oriental rugs. Chairs and benches are available, and book browsers may stay in the store as long as they like—they are encouraged to leisurely pursue the books that interest them. There is even a small Zen garden at the side of the building.

The owners of the Bodhi Tree, Phil and Elsa Thompson and Stan and Fran Madson, think of their store as a refuge from the hustle and bustle of the city with its attendant needs and drives. All the people who work in the store are involved in some type of spiritual development and are able to provide information and answer questions about specific metaphysical disciplines.

Near the Bodhi Tree is a Sikh Center, under the direction of Yogi Bhajan, and the store is often visited by turbaned, regal-looking Sikhs. The store is so perfectly "type-cast" as a spiritual center that it was once used as a set for a motion picture. A number of actors and actresses frequent the shop in the belief that the ability to act is the ability to be free of past conditioning; they therefore search out books that will aid their self-development.

Although the store does not issue a catalogue, the staff will service all mail-order requests, and the shop does occasionally mail out specialized book lists. The staff will also special order books the store does not carry and notify customers when out-of-stock books arrive at the store.

The philosophy of the store, apparent in the decor and in the quality and variety of the stock, was summed up by one of the owners: "We have tried to keep the Bodhi Tree open and neutral to the sundry philosophies and religions that exist and for which we carry books. We expect all the people who work in the store to respect this concept. It is unreasonable to deride other people's ideas, religious beliefs, practices, or preferences. As Swami Satchidananda once said, 'Truth is one. Paths are many.' "

8585 Melrose Avenue, Los Angeles, California 90069; Tel. 213-659-1733. Hours: seven days a week, 11:00 A.M.–11:00 P.M.; used book branch, seven days a week, 11:00 A.M.–7:00 P.M.

KEPLER'S BOOKS AND MAGAZINES   MENLO PARK CALIFORNIA

When Mimi Farina, a folk singer and the sister of Joan Baez, performed at Kepler's a few years ago it was to help her friend Ira Sandperl, the scheduled guest author, who was hospitalized due to a bicycle accident. Her appearance attracted over one hundred people to the store, an occurrence that seemed almost a natural part of Kepler's business day. Kepler's is well known, not only as the bookstore that has probably the largest paperback stock in the country, but also as one of the most active, politically and in a literary manner, in its sponsorship of discussions with authors and other events. These celebrations are of an idea that caught on, a vision that was welcomed by the people of the Menlo Park/Palo Alto area. Kepler's is a bookstore where one can browse undisturbed through an enormous collection of paperback books, then relax in a reading room with a cup of coffee, a pastry, a good book.

This was the idea that led Roy Kepler to open Kepler's Books and Magazines in May of 1955 next to the Guild Theater in Menlo Park.

The idea was a good one: within four years the store had moved three times into increasingly larger buildings, until it settled at its present location.

There were frequent meetings at the store in those years with authors who discussed their books and ideas. Among those who appeared were C. P. Snow, Felix Greene, Ken Kesey, Theodore Roszak, Paul Jacobs, Joan Baez, Ammon Hennacy, and David McReynolds.

In 1964 Kepler's expanded again, this time by the addition of a second store, in Palo Alto. The Menlo Park story was repeated: the store outgrew itself and moved to its present location at the Village Corners, El Camino and San Antonio Road.

And the growth continues. Recently, Walter Schreck retired from his auto shop business, and Kepler's annexed the building he had occupied, located behind the bookstore: sixty more shelves for books, over twice the previous floor space, and a new, larger Browser's Room, with coffee, soft drinks, pastry, and comfortable chairs and tables.

The store meetings will once again become frequent, with a number of authors already scheduled to appear.

Roy Kepler's vision of a friendly, well-stocked bookstore continues, changing only to meet the needs of an increasing population. From the first small store run by Roy and Patricia Kepler to the present operation—two stores and a staff of twenty-eight people supervised by general manager Ralph Kohn and Palo Alto manager Betty Sumrall—the aim has remained constant.

Pay a visit to Kepler's. You'll have fun, and you may even find that book you've been meaning to get for awhile.

Kepler's philosophy of bookselling is libertarian: "We try to make available the full range of ideas good and bad, left and right; whatever interests humankind. In a democracy, people must learn to make choices. They cannot do that unless they know what the choices are."

825 El Camino Real, Menlo Park, California 94025; Tel. 415-324-4321. Hours: Monday–Thursday, 10:00 A.M.–11:00 P.M.; Friday and Saturday, 10:00 A.M.–Midnight; Sunday, Noon–11:00 P.M. There is a second store, also called Kepler's Books and Magazines, at: Village Corners Shopping Center, San Antonio Road & El Camino Real, Los Altos, California 94022. Hours: Monday–Saturday, 10:00 A.M.–9:00 P.M.; Sunday, Noon–9:00 P.M.

ONCE UPON A TIME
MONTROSE CALIFORNIA

A bell tinkles at the door; there is a hint of lavender sachet; a brightly colored braided rug graces the floor; there are huge stuffed animals in various parts of the store; books are shelved and spread about in organized clutter; the owner, Jane Humphrey, sits in a rocking chair, knitting. This is a warm, friendly, children's bookstore, nestled in the foothills of the Crescenta-Canada Valley, some sixteen miles north of Los Angeles.

"I found a magic place in Montrose," said an eleven-year-old to his parents at dinner, shortly after the store opened. This kind of reaction is a typical one from children after paying a visit to the store. Jane Humphrey's charming and understanding ways captivate children, as do the puppet shows, storytime, mime performances, and occasional special films she offers.

Once Upon A Time, Montrose, California

Once Upon A Time has become one of the favorite spots for the local children to go. Even their parents like it.

The store carries some five thousand books, all new, all hardbound and paper, fiction and nonfiction. There are also prints, calendars, toys, games, dolls, and other items that relate to children's literature for sale. The store issues a monthly newsletter, and anyone who requests it can be placed on the list.

Ms. Humphrey says that the adults and children who frequent her shop "view life with wonder and still believe in magic." She attempts to balance the elements of surprise, fascination, and education through one of the best selections of children's books in California.

2309 Honolulu Ave., Montrose, California 91020; Tel. 213-248-9668. Hours: Monday–Friday, 10:00 A.M.–10:30 P.M.; Saturday, 10:00 A.M.–5:30 P.M.; closed Sunday.

PENINSULA BOOK SHOP

PALO ALTO CALIFORNIA

Owners Bud Lorentz and Harold Harvey like to think of the Peninsula Book Shop as an "old-fashioned" bookstore, and by the degree of personal service and friendliness offered, it certainly qualifies. The staff is highly knowledgeable; they encourage browsers and gladly answer all questions. It's a charmingly small store, but with plenty of books in stock—some eighteen to twenty thousand titles—located in a pleasant shopping center constructed of redwood timbers with red tile roofs and planted walking areas. Large, old shade trees cool the area right outside the store, and it's a two-minute walk to the campus of Stanford University. The interior of the store is finished in unpainted redwood beams and natural wood, rustic shelving.

The Peninsula Book Shop is a general bookstore and it carries new hardcover and paperbound books, both fiction and nonfiction, of all kinds and classifications. As special services, the store provides worldwide mailing and free gift-wrapping, and the staff will search for books and will also special order any book that is in print. The shop conducts two sales a year—in May and October—and also has author autograph parties from time to time. A mailing list is maintained, and anyone can be placed on it by writing to the store. Both Master Charge and Visa credit cards are accepted. "Chainstores and discount stores are making it difficult for the small, independent bookstore," says Lorentz, "so we must rely on prompt special-order service and courteous treatment of customers."

82 Town and Country Village, Palo Alto, California 94301; Tel. 415-326-0880. Hours: Monday–Saturday, 9:30 A.M.–5:30 P.M.; Thursdays, till 9:00 P.M.

THE ALBATROSS BOOK STORE   SAN FRANCISCO CALIFORNIA

James Russell Lowell said, "There is a sense of security in an old book which Time has criticized for us!" That may account, in part, for the delight of roaming through used book stores, poring over dusty volumes and leafing gingerly through browning, brittle pages.

The Albatross offers such delights, with a unique bonus: with roughly 200,000 books in stock, the shop still manages to be probably the most orderly used bookstore in the country. Owners Donald Sharp and Joel Chapman have a penchant for maintaining logical categories, and they claim to have been blessed with a staff that does a heroic job of keeping order, despite the rapid changing of stock, for the Albatross not only sells used books, it also buys, sells and trades books, magazines, and paperbacks, and buys book collections from estates and libraries.

All of the staff are extremely knowledgeable about books in general, and about their stock in particular. They will efficiently direct you to books or back issues of magazines in the subject of your choice, all neatly stacked and easy to look through. Or ask them for a specific title; if it's in stock, the salespeople can locate it immediately.

If your book is not available, the store will search for it and notify you once they've found it. They'll search for out-of-print books, as well. The Albatross also maintains a customer "Want File," so that when a book you've been yearning for finally comes their way, the store will put it aside and notify you. There is no charge for this service, and no obligation to buy any book.

The Albatross carries used books in all areas, but it specializes in modern first editions, science fiction, mysteries, books by Jack London, books on ships and the sea, aviation, and illustrated children's books. The store offers a frequently updated catalog and lists of its current stock to customers upon request. There is no charge to be put on the mailing list for the catalog, and browsing through it can be almost as fascinating as wandering through the aisles. The current catalog offers books in twenty-six categories, including: Americana (San Francisciana; Californiana; the West; Indiana; Eastern Americana); Aviation; Costumery; Fantasy–Science Fiction; Flags and Maps; Hunting and Fishing; Ships and the Sea; Illustrated Books (and here they carry some limited editions, collectors' items); Literature; Medicine; Nature; Show Business; Photography; Railroading; Religion and the Occult; and Sports.

Most books are in good or very good condition. Any exceptions are noted in the catalog, or acknowledged in the store.

The store also sells prints, posters, maps, postcards, old

27

photos, sheet music, and magazines. There is an annual sale.

The Albatross is frequently busy. It's a browser's haven, located right in downtown San Francisco, only one block from the famous cable car turntable at the foot of Powell and Market streets. The building itself is one of the city's oldest, dating back to just after the devastating earthquake and fire of April 1906. It's easy to get to, by cable car or subway (BART), or by automobile; there is ample parking in the lot next to the store.

Remember that the Albatross is as interested in buying as in selling. Donald Sharp says: "Books are our best friends, and we think of ourselves as keepers of them and as a way station in their preservation from one generation to the next. We fix up the battered ones and protect the beautiful."

So don't hesitate to bring in your books, or your book list. The Albatross will make you a cash or trade offer. If you're like us, you can exchange your old books for some new old books.

166 Eddy Street (corner Taylor), San Francisco, California 94102; Tel: 415-885-6501; Hours: 10:00 A.M.–6:00 P.M. weekdays, and 11:00 A.M.–6:00 P.M. on Saturday. Closed Sunday.

Given four hundred and five years, and an ordinary man can in the ordinary course, without any undue haste or putting any pressure upon his taste, surround himself with two thousand books, all in his own language, and thenceforward have at least one place in the world in which it is possible to be happy.

AUGUSTINE BIRRELL

CITY LIGHTS BOOKSTORE

"I saw the best minds of my generation destroyed by madness, starving hysterical naked . . ." went the first line of *Howl*, originally published by City Lights in a collection of Allen Ginsberg's poetry in the early 1950s. The poem was responsible for many things: it became the rallying call for and helped to officially usher in the Beat Generation; it was the cause of a celebrated censorship trial which ultimately affected the nation's obscenity laws; it propelled Ginsberg, City Lights Bookstore, and its owner, Lawrence Ferlinghetti, into national prominence. For the beatniks of the 1950s, City Lights Books became their spiritual home, a bookstore that carried the avant-garde poetry and prose that they wanted to read, the first bookstore in America to sell only paperbacks (which the frugal could buy), and a store that became known for occasionally turning the other way when a young poet stole a book because he simply had to have it, but could not afford it.

The police arrested Ferlinghetti and manager Shigeyoshi Murao for publishing and selling *Howl,* and the subsequent trial brought out some of the country's foremost literati to the defense: Mark Schorer, Vincent McHugh, Kenneth Rexroth, among many others. The *San Francisco Chronicle* said of the spectacle: "There were probably more beards and baggy jackets and more copies of the *Partisan Review* than the Hall of Justice had seen in its history." Eventually, Ferlinghetti and the book were cleared.

Located between Chinatown and North Beach, both tourist and high-traffic areas, City Lights is always crowded with browsers. Naturally, it has a strong poetry section and also has substantial stock in psychology, fiction, drama and film, fantasy and science fiction, the humanities, small press editions— American and foreign—and underground periodicals.

29

City Lights looks so much like what it is—a store that sells avant-garde, radical, and underground literature—that it was used as a set in the filming of *The Subterraneans*, a movie about beat life in San Francisco based on the novel of the same name by Jack Kerouac, author of the famous *On The Road*. During the store's early years, Kerouac often frequented City Lights and was a good friend of Ferlinghetti's.

Again, in 1966, the store became entangled in legal problems: a clerk was arrested for selling a book of erotic poems, *The Love Book*, while other stores in the city were carrying the same book and were not being prosecuted. Ferlinghetti went to court and complained that his bookstore was kept under constant surveillance and that this was both unfair and unconstitutional. Eventually, the case was dropped.

The United States is one of the few countries in the world that could produce, accommodate, and allow a bookstore such as City Lights. But is it really a bookstore? We think of it as a state of mind: colorful, compelling, irreverent, and totally American.

261 Columbus Avenue at Broadway, San Francisco, California 94133; Tel. 415-362-8193. Hours: seven days a week, "To midnight or later."

THE BOOK DEN   SANTA BARBARA
                                        CALIFORNIA

The first time novelist Edward Dahlberg came into the Book Den, he charged the store with his own personal brand of electricity: talking to the customers, buying books, asking questions, quizzing the store owners, spewing philosophy, checking on whether they had any copies of his book *The Confessions of Edward Dahlberg* or some of his out-of-print works. He came back often. There are a number of other authors who live in the area who also visit, browse, and buy at the Book Den, the oldest bookstore in Santa Barbara, opened over forty years ago in a building once used as an automobile garage.

The Book Den has a large stock of general books—over thirty-five thousand in all—but also carries old magazines (some dating as far back as the 1890s), old postcards, prints, records, comics, maps, and assorted nostalgia, filling over fifty-four drawers. Although the store does not issue a catalog, the staff will fill all mail orders.

The Book Den is easy, almost fun, to find: across the street from the public library, one block from the county courthouse, and across the street from the art museum. There is public parking behind the store, and it is located near other bookstores and a number of restaurants, making the area a pleasant place to stroll and shop.

The owners, Richard and Susan Phelps, assisted by Nancy Lynch, often make buying trips to find interesting out-of-print books, memorabilia, and nostalgia items. They make no attempt to build a specialty, but try to have all kinds of books for all kinds of people in their store. They succeed. "We enjoy books," says Mrs. Phelps.

15 East Anapamu, Santa Barbara, California 93102; Tel. 805-962-3321. Hours: Monday–Saturday, 9:30 A.M.–5:30 P.M.

PLAZA BOOKS/ PAPER VISION

SANTA CRUZ CALIFORNIA

Three-quarters of a century ago, the Hotel Metropole in Santa Cruz was the pride of the city and charged fifty cents a day for any one of its forty-eight rooms. The ground floor was occupied by a real-estate broker, a dry-goods business, and a millinery shop, and over the years the history of Santa Cruz has

31

been inexorably intertwined with the building. Today, the hotel is no longer operative; the other businesses have moved out; and Plaza Books, a general bookstore, and Paper Vision, a poster and print shop, have taken over the site. The bookshop—originally founded in 1910—had lived in a number of locations and has a rich history of its own. Now, the wedding of two histories—building and business—makes Plaza Books one of the most interesting bookshops in California.

The store has an enormous paperback section, the titles of which have been carefully selected to appeal to the students from the nearby University of California at Santa Cruz and to the constantly growing tourist trade. The graphic section is unmatched in its range—from popular posters to medium-priced art items from various museum publishers. The atmosphere is charming and courteous, and the clerks will do everything possible to help a customer find the right book.

"We believe we have one of the finest bookstores in Western America," say Barbara and Hal Morris, the owners. They may be right.

1111 Pacific Avenue, Santa Cruz, California 95060; Tel. 408-425-1111. Hours: Monday–Saturday, 9:00 A.M.–9:00 P.M.; Sundays, 11:00 A.M.–5:00 P.M.

SCENE OF THE CRIME   SHERMAN OAKS CALIFORNIA

It is a Sunday afternoon and the room is unmistakably Victorian: red carpeting, flocked wallpaper, a roll-top desk amidst other antique furniture, pillows appliquéd with figures bearing a striking resemblance to Hercule Poirot and Sherlock Holmes. Guests are greeted at the door by Ruth Windfeldt, dressed in a long, turn-of-the-century dress. She is gracious, other-worldly. Her hair is elegantly Gibsonian. A sterling silver tray of homemade cookies sits atop the buffet table. Wine is served and everyone sits back and listens to the reading of an esoteric mystery story, *The Methods of Uncle Abner*, whose hero is a pre-Civil War, West Virginian squire.

If this sounds like a scene out of Dickens, it's supposed to—but it's actually a typical tableau that takes place regularly at the Scene of the Crime, a bookstore that specializes in murder mysteries, detective, crime, and suspense action. Here, with the store's stock of some eight thousand titles, it's possible to find all the works of Agatha Christie, Raymond Chandler, Ruth Rendell, Cornell Woolrich, and thousands of other new and used books concerning crime.

If there is any question about how seriously Scene of the Crime integrates itself into the life of the detective novel, note the offering of mystery tours: Raymond Chandler's Los Angeles; Dashiell Hammett's San Francisco; Dorothy Sayers' England; and the Egypt of Agatha Christie's *Death on the Nile*.

13636 Ventura Blvd., Sherman Oaks, California 91423; Tel. 213-981-CLUE. Hours: Tuesday–Saturday, 10:00 A.M.–6:00 P.M.; Friday until 9:00 P.M.

Colorado

BRILLIG WORKS BOOK STORE

BOULDER COLORADO

A customer once wrote to the Brillig Works, saying: "Of all the bookstores I have visited, yours has the most relaxed atmosphere. It is laid out in such a way that the customer gets lost and doesn't care, because everywhere he turns is another interesting section of books to look at." Indeed, the Brillig has four floors, seven rooms, four staircases, twists and turns everywhere, and books, books, and more books. As is the city of Boulder, it is located in the shadow of the Rocky Mountains.

There is no pretentious formality at the Brillig Works. The owners, Tim Long and Larry McKay, invite their customers to relax on an old, overstuffed sofa and comfortable chairs and actually read a book before deciding to buy it. Their philosophy is to be "loose on the outside but have an inner core of strength and efficiency. We have a strict inventory control system and budget, for example."

The Brillig Works sells all categories of books, except used. The owners deal with over three hundred publishers to maintain a large selection of varied titles, rather than stock many copies of a few books. The store has an excellent poetry section and enough books on metaphysics to please any seeker. As special services, the staff will order books for customers and service mail-order accounts. The shop sponsors autograph parties, seminars, and even a film series. There is no charge for being placed on the store's mailing list, and Master Charge and Visa credit cards are accepted.

There seems to be always something happening at the Brillig Works. The store has sponsored video interviews for the Boulder Public Library with such people as novelist John Gardner and Ezra Pound's daughter, Mary de Rachewiltz, who read from her father's cantos.

Anaïs Nin once came to the Brillig for an autographing and gave a lecture. Other writers who have browsed the Brillig include Gregory Bateson, Allen Ginsberg, William Burroughs, E. L. Doctorow, R. Sukenick, C. Major, Allen Dugan, Ishmael Reed, and William Matthews.

Larry says that during the course of any given day he drinks a lot of wine, takes a three-hour lunch, stocks shelves, pays bills, cleans floors, talks with customers, orders books, and tries to "keep it all together." Tim says that although he still likes to eat, he has given up wine for *clarity*.

1322 College Avenue, Boulder, Colorado 80302; Tel. 303-443-7461. Hours: Monday–Saturday, 9:30 A.M.–6:00 P.M.

THE CHINOOK BOOKSHOP   COLORADO SPRINGS COLORADO

Thoroughly dedicated to customer service is the Chinook Bookshop in Colorado Springs. It's owned and operated by Dick and Judy Noyes, who founded the shop in 1959 and now employ some twelve to fifteen people. The stock consists of about twenty thousand hardbound titles, thirty thousand paperbacks. The shop sells fiction and nonfiction, as well as remainders, but does not handle used books at all. The Chinook is a general bookstore, and an excellent one.

It's in the area of special services that this shop really shines. The special-order department for foreign and out-of-print books does not require a down payment; personal checks are accepted from all over, with no ID; free delivery to in-town hospitals is offered; discounts are given to school and church libraries; and a two-story playhouse in the children's department keeps youngsters occupied while parents browse. There is always free coffee, and brandy is served with the coffee on special occasions. The Chinook is open on Sunday afternoons from Thanksgiving to Christmas, serving sherry or rum punch. The store offers free gift-wrapping, will mail anywhere, and provides for free parking and free bus rides.

Book promotions, in the form of receptions for local authors who have produced important books, are done on occasion, but the emphasis here is on the word "important." "Currents from the Chinook" is an excellent and informative newsletter that this shop publishes. It's extremely well done, and you can get on the mailing list simply by requesting it.

Unusual, specially chosen greeting cards are always in stock and account for 5 percent of the shop's annual sales. Maps and globes make up another 4 percent. The shop accepts Master Charge and Visa.

Dick Noyes is a past president of the American Booksellers Association; his wife, Judy, serves as a consultant to the Children's Book Council and is on an ABA committee serving as liaison between children's booksellers and children's book editors; she has reviewed children's books for *Publisher's Weekly* and the *New York Times*.

Jane Emery, Chinook's paperback manager for eighteen years, serves on the retail advisory committee for Bantam Books and on the ABA's basic paperback committee.

Dick tells of one request that had him—for awhile, anyway—stumped. A young lady came to the store asking for a "braddle bobble." Seeing the blank looks, she expounded on her request. She wanted a "watt braddle bobble." The message finally came through. This southern miss was in search of a "white bridal bible." The order was happily filled.

"We want to be the best," Dick Noyes says. We're not sure he hasn't already gotten there.

210 No. Tejon, Colorado Springs, Colorado 80903; Tel. 303-635-

5500. *Hours: Monday–Friday, 9:30 A.M.–5:30 P.M.; Saturday, 9:30 A.M.–4:30 P.M.*

POOH CORNER BOOK STORE

DENVER COLORADO

As the name of the store implies—and it's a trademark name, the only store in the country permitted to use it—the speciality is in children's books, and it is one of the oldest stores to carry a preponderance of juvenile literature (it was founded in 1928). Inside is a cozy, friendly shop, with bright yellow and red walls, and a genial and cluttered atmosphere. Stuffed versions of Winnie, Eeyore, and Tigger are prominently displayed, and there are pictures on the walls of Pooh reaching for books instead of his traditional honey.

In addition to children's books, the Pooh Corner also carries a carefully chosen selection of adult books, art and music books, and books concerning Colorado. It also sells greeting cards.

The store is fifteen minutes from downtown Denver and close to an exclusive residential area. Under the guidance of owner W. L. Stevens, the staff gives personal attention to customers in the selection of children's books.

16 Cherry Creek Shopping Center, Denver, Colorado 80206; Tel. 303-399-1652. Hours: Monday–Saturday, 9:30 A.M.–5:30 P.M.; Thursday, 9:30 A.M.–8:00 P.M.

All books are either dreams or swords.

AMY LOWELL

37

Connecticut

WHITLOCK FARM BOOK BARN

BETHANY CONNECTICUT

We asked Gilbert Whitlock what he does in a typical day. Here is his answer:

"Get up at 6:00 A.M.—work for an hour or so in the garden (putting beanpoles now) or at my desk at home. Have breakfast at 7:15. Work another hour in the garden or around the house. Go down to the book-barns at 8:00, work in the garden there, or, if it's raining, at my desk 'til 9:00, when we open. From 9:00 to 12:00, I *try* to catalog books at my desk, but sometimes get only a few listed because of incessant telephone calls and friendly visitors who like to talk (I do too)—thus, most of the cataloging falls on Muriel, our overworked office manager, cataloger, accountant, nurse, etc.

"At twelve noon I leave for the pole barn across the field, where I have my Campbell's soup lunch and work undisturbed at cataloging, pricing, sorting, etc. The pole barn is one hundred feet long and thirty feet wide and is used for storing new acquisitions and old overstock. (We usually wind up giving this to church sales and such.) If I have a 'book call,' I leave after lunch and go to whatever part of the state my calendar calls me to. If I'm in luck, I don't buy any books and get back to work in the huge logjam we always have piled up. If I do buy books, they get piled up in the car and unloaded on my return. If it's a large quantity, I make an appointment for my son to pick them up later.

"If I spend my afternoon in the pole barn (not often), as soon after 5:00 P.M. (our closing time) as I see all the cars have gone, I return to the 'turkey house'—our main building—and if the

38

gardening isn't too pressing, I work for a couple of hours at my desk with a pillow over the infernal telephone and the record player turned up pretty high, with music that *I* like—rock and roll and Muzak have no chance at this hour—and at 7:00 (my wife will say it's 7:30), I go home and have dinner on the porch. The night noises get noisier as 8:00 P.M. approaches, but it's still the pleasantest noise of the day. We may stay on the porch and Hope will read until 10:00 when we usually go indoors to hear the TV news and have a cracker and cheese snack. We usually go to bed at 11:00 with Mary Hartman, but we hardly ever stay awake to know what's going on with those folks."

The shop was founded by Whitlock in 1945 and now employs eight people full time, plus three additional clerks on a part-time basis. There are all kinds of books in the general stock, which totals some fifty thousand to seventy-five thousand books. The store specializes in children's books, Connecticut history, natural history, and rare, curious, and old Americana. There is a place for picnics, and school groups come out for story readings once a week. The store sends out three or four lists a month, and you can get on the mailing list just by asking. There's no charge. Oddly enough, they do service mail orders, but find it hard to keep up with the demand.

This shop, consisting of three large barns in rolling, green pastureland, has Hereford cows (now with seven calves in toto) and, in the upper barn, a print loft with thousands of prints and maps. A pleasant day can be spent driving up through the fall foliage to this lovely spot just four miles off the Wilbur Cross Expressway.

The intention of the owners is to provide worthwhile books at a very low cost—they still have plenty of good five-and-ten-centers—and to provide a place where people will be happy to come and will feel at home. They're just as glad to see people who don't buy as they are to welcome those who do.

In the beginning, back in the forties, Gilbert began collecting books and storing them about the house. When the house became too cluttered and the family began to complain, he began filling the farm buildings with books.

He sold books to other booksellers and built a thriving business in mail order, but in 1953 a fire struck and destroyed most of the books; then, slowly, the business was built back up again. When the Whitlocks decided to "go public," the shop was operated on the honor system, with a plain cigar box at the top of the stairs for people to deposit their money. After a while they found out that youngsters were "borrowing" the money, and they began to use a hinged cigar box so that the kids couldn't see the cash. This served for a year or longer, until they discovered that older children were raiding the box on their way to high school.

The barn had no lock and was open and lighted twenty-four hours of every day. Insomniacs would show up in the middle of the night to read. Early risers could be seen poring over the shelves at 5:00 A.M. Finally, and sadly, the cigar box had to be given up. Thieves and shoplifters signaled the end of an era, and a padlock had to be put on the barn door.

Bargains? If you have the patience to hunt and you know what to look for, you can find them here. Take the book that was sold for a dollar or so, a volume of Goethe's works; it was in poor condition, the binding was torn, and some contemporary scholar had scribbled pencil notes in the margins. The book went through the hands of several other book dealers, and was finally bought by a student for ten dollars. He suspected the notes in the margins might prove interesting, and he was right. Those were, indeed, Goethe's own scribblings, and that book finally sold for thouands of dollars.

Things are getting to be more and more difficult, for increased costs, rising postal rates, and the ever-increasing shoplifting may soon spell an end to this delightful operation. Closing the shop, however, is anathema to the Whitlocks, for to them bookselling is not just a business, it's a way of life.

20 Sperry Road, Bethany, Connecticut 06525; Tel. 203-393-1240. Hours: Tuesday–Sunday, 9:00 A.M.–5:00 P.M.

COBBLE COURT BOOKSHOP

LITCHFIELD CONNECTICUT

Litchfield, Connecticut, is a charming old town in the grand Down-East manner. Small shops dot the area, and the beautifully kept old homes are separated by stone fences, erected in the seventeenth and eighteenth centuries. The houses, mostly featuring white clapboard siding, overlook rolling hills, velvet lawns, and old elm trees that shade the whole. As you drive down the sleepy streets, you taste the flavor of Americana, and you know that behind those closed doors, each house must be a repository of antiques that would make any museum of early Americana blanch with envy.

Nestled in this richness is the Cobble Court Bookshop. L. M. Wiggin owns the shop now, having acquired it in 1975. The store, with some eight thousand books in stock, sells new and used hardback and paperbound books, fiction as well as nonfiction, although the emphasis is on nonfiction books. It's classed as a general bookshop. Many bookstore services are offered, including book search and autograph parties.

The people who come to this shop cross all age groups and all incomes, but they aren't strong for hardcover books of fiction. They do enjoy nature books, and no wonder, for all about them in this town, nature abounds. It's a first-rate service shop, stocked with more than adequate variety in a fascinating building in an historic town. The building is actually a converted blacksmith's shop.

In addition to books, the store offers a few toys, notepapers, and records. The philosophy is to offer service to each customer, no matter how small, and then follow up. The *New York*

41

Times recently described this as a friendly store. We heartily agree.

Cobble Court Bookshop, Litchfield, Connecticut 06759; Tel. 203-567-0084. Hours: Monday–Saturday, 9:00 A.M.–5:00 P.M.

NEW CANAAN BOOK SHOP   NEW CANAAN CONNECTICUT

In the affluent, highly literate town of New Canaan, bookstores are almost as common as gas stations in Detroit. But this one is special. It began, in the summer of 1958, as a tiny shop in an historic white frame building. Now it has expanded to many times the original area.

Because its customers have a wide variety of interests and cover a broad age range, New Canaan Book Shop is careful to stock books in many subject areas. The stock of approximately *twenty thousand* titles is all new books, hardback and paperback, but the store will search for books its customers request and will even try to obtain out-of-print books, when possible. The shop also maintains a rental library, a welcome rarity in bookstores. There's a bit of a waiting list for current best sellers, of course, but the library also provides some of the classics and some good standard fiction and nonfiction books.

The shop puts out an annual Christmas catalog, and will mail one free to customers on its mailing list; you may simply request that your name be added to the list.

Although books make up 80 percent of the store's stock, it also sells stationery and greeting cards, personally imprinted if you so request, along with bookends and selected maps. Orders may be paid for via Master Charge or Visa charge cards.

Other service "extras" include free gift-wrapping, gift list consultation and handling, and fast, dependable special ordering. The store will mail books anywhere.

42

Thomas and Marguerite Whitney, who have owned the New Canaan Book Shop since 1972, guide their capable staff to provide excellent service to each customer. The store encourages its personnel to read widely themselves, so that they will be better able to "get each person together with the right book." Employees are even encouraged to attend bookselling events (often with all expenses paid by the store) and Booksellers' School, and the staff's pride in its ability to help each customer is evident—and deserved.

Mr. Whitney defines bookselling as "an unusual mix of art and business. We must encourage reading, at all levels and in all areas. Our work is not only encouraging and servicing the present reader, but finding and introducing the nonreader."

In its much expanded quarters, the new New Canaan Book Shop should be even better equipped to do just that.

59 Elm Street, New Canaan, Connecticut 06840; Tel. 203-966-1684. Hours: Monday–Friday, 9:00 A.M.–5:30 P.M.; Saturday, 9:00 A.M.– 5:00 P.M.

THE FOUNDRY BOOKSTORE   NEW HAVEN CONNECTICUT

This bookshop was once a foundry, and the wall is decorated with some of the old patterns of the ironwork that was made there. It later became a rug shop, then a decorating store, and finally saw the light as the Channel Bookshop, run by two maiden ladies who one day called Mary Reigeluth—the present owner—and asked if she'd like to buy the store. Mary explained at the time that she would love to, but had four little children—perhaps they could call again in twenty years?

The store went to somebody else, failed, and was about to be torn down when the New Haven Council of the Arts bought and restored it. The Reigeluths bought it shortly afterwards. The area blossomed, and now includes the Munson Gallery, the Neighborhood Music School, and the Creative Arts Workshop. It's become a small cultural complex, has a music store, and now a little park is being built in back so they can have outdoor concerts and the store can open onto the park.

The store has four employees and stocks fifteen to sixteen thousand books. It has a full line of children's books and works by local authors, and carries fiction and nonfiction, hard and soft cover, new books only.

It has a library-like atmosphere; there's room to sit and read, and special small chairs and a table for children. The Foundry does not search for out-of-print books, but if such a request comes in, it is referred to a friend who will. Mail orders are accepted. In addition to books, there is a limited collection of carefully selected cards. Autograph parties feature sherry and crackers. When Maurice Sendak appeared, there were five hundred people in attendance. The clientele is varied, but thanks to the propinquity of Yale, the store counts many retired professors, such as Cleanth Brooks and others, among its customers, and the staff does a great deal of ordering for Yale professors. The shop is also supportive of local authors—a young doctor who teaches at the medical college and who wrote a book on internship comes in with her hospital beeper in her skirt pocket.

"There are more psychiatrists and psychologists per square head than anywhere else, and we have many different requests for all *kinds* of books," Ms. Reigeluth explains. "Henry, the young manager, is more liberal—I'm more traditional. It's an interesting combination. He's read everything since 1920, I've read everything up to then!"

33 Whitney Avenue, New Haven, Connecticut 06510; Tel. 203-624-8282. Hours: Monday–Saturday, 9:30 A.M.–5:30 P.M.

YALE CO-OP

NEW HAVEN
CONNECTICUT

Founded in the 1800s by the students and faculty of Yale University, the Co-op is one of the most complete bookstores in the country for new books of every kind: over 200,000 volumes are kept in stock at all times. The store also contains substantial selections of poetry, literature, criticism, foreign books, technical books, and law books. There is a year-round bargain section of extremely high-quality books, and there is a separate department which is thoroughly stocked to meet the scholastic demands of the students of the university. The Co-op accepts Visa credit cards and Master Charge.

We interviewed Ted Wilentz, general manager of the store, a former president of the American Booksellers Association and former owner of New York's famed Eighth Street Bookshop, about the Yale Co-op and his philosophy of bookselling:

I have very definite ideas about what a bookstore should do and be. It is one of the great cultural forces. Henry Steele Commager said that a university bookstore is a department within a university. A good student spends more time there than in any one class. The first thing a bookstore should offer its patrons is a good stock, whether specialized or general in nature. Secondly, the store should offer the knowledge of its staff, and thirdly, a store should have an identifiable style, character, or tone. In the Yale Co-op, there is an immediate sense of very large stock, the Grolier has a different feeling, City Lights yet another atmosphere. Walden's has the tendency to standardize: a store should have a flavor and it's all right if it's pepper *and* salt.

In the displays at the Co-op, I try to show scholarly books without intimidating the so-called middlebrow, but the approach is to reflect what I call the tone of "honest intellectualism." Part of the function of the bookseller is to present to the customer what is old and good and what is new and good. We try to stay ahead of the reader, we attempt to, what is more important, excite the person who comes into our store. The point is to make book buying an experience, not just the purchasing but the browsing, too.

45

The Yale Co-op is a $6 million business, the third largest retailing establishment of any kind in New Haven, and each year more and more books are sold. In a university environment, things do not always go smoothly, however: a conservative alumnus wrote to the store asking why they carried certain "inflammatory" works. Wilentz was compelled to compile a long list of conservative books that were carried by the store, including those of Yale alumnus William F. Buckley. "As a bookseller, you have the right to make certain choices as to what you will or will not carry," he said. "You can't please everyone, although you may try."

Yale Co-op, 77 Broadway, New Haven, Connecticut 06520. Hours: Monday–Saturday, 9:15 A.M.–5:30 P.M.; Thursday till 9:00 P.M.

THE BOOKSTORE OF OLD GREENWICH
OLD GREENWICH CONNECTICUT

Retailing is a guessing game. The store owner or manager must try to predict what items will sell, and in what quantities, and stock his shelves accordingly. This requires a large amount of capital, considerable risk, and a lot of shelf space, for most stores try very hard not to run out of fast-selling merchandise. It usually takes so long to get single quantities of items on special order from the manufacturer or the wholesaler that the customer winds up becoming angry at the store.

Now meet the exception to the rule. The Bookstore of Old Greenwich, only two-and-a-half years old, was established by Van and Nancy Messner, a young husband and wife who seem to be as happy about the fact that they're working together as they are about being able to work at something they both love to do. Starting with a limited amount of capital, they decided to abandon the usual rule of stocking multiple copies of fast-moving titles. Instead, they have only one or two copies of each title, whether hardback or paper; this allows them to stock a great variety of different books. The Bookstore currently has in excess of fifteen thousand paperbacks and nearly two thousand hardbacks, all new books, both fiction and nonfiction.

The Messners can do this because they are quite conveniently located close to two major book wholesalers. Van makes several buying trips each week to pick up books customers have ordered and to see what's new. The result is that the Bookstore has the largest paperback selection in the county, and one of the largest selections of hardbound books. And if a customer orders a book that's out of stock, 80 percent of the time the store gets the book within five working days; sometimes, that very afternoon.

The Bookstore carries all of the current best sellers, many books of popular fiction and mysteries, has a particularly good literature and fiction section, many titles in areas of local interest, such as cooking, sailing, and tennis, and an extensive collection of poetry. For children, there is a large selection of paperbacks and a small selection of juvenile hardcovers; there's also a paperback young adults section. The Messners read extensively and provide a fund of information to customers; they particularly recommend books they themselves enjoyed reading.

Periodically, they prepare handouts for their customers, listing new titles and starring the books they personally recommend. They maintain a "co-op plan"—each customer is urged to save his receipts, and once he has accumulated receipts for $50 in purchases, he gets 10 percent off the next purchase. The store also carries a large stock of remaindered books—hardbound books, often large format, with radically discounted prices.

The Bookstore also sells Lego toys, fine coloring books and pencils, maps, cards, educational toys, and jigsaw puzzles. (At one point a puzzle lay on a table in the store; customers would walk by, stop to fit in a piece, and get hooked.) The store is very

47

bright and airy, filled with plants and light-wood shelves that Van made himself. A plush corduroy sofa, with copies of the *New York Times Book Review* nearby, provides a soft reading nook, but customers are apt to sit on the carpeted floor to browse through some interesting titles. At those times, they're often visited by Quezal, the Messners' bluepoint Siamese cat, who is the official store mascot (and who seems, diplomatically, to be able to sense which visitors do not favor feline companionship).

The Bookstore holds two sales a year. In July, the Messners join other Old Greenwich merchants for the town sidewalk sale, and in January there is the Christmas cleanup sale. The store accepts major charge cards.

The Messners have a unique sense of responsibility about their book selecting. "For example, we didn't stock *Show Me*, because it's not an educational book but, rather, one more designed for grown-ups, it's dishonest. And we haven't stocked some of the Nixon books. But if the book is an attempt to be honest, even if we disagree with it, we'll stock it—like the Colson book, for example. We may disagree with Colson, but he's telling the truth as he sees it, so we've stocked him." But if a customer requests a book they don't stock, they will special order it.

People come in and ask their advice on what books to buy for various purposes: "What's an appropriate gift?" "What's the best book to read on a train?" "What's the best book you've read in the last three months?"

And, according to the owners of the Bookstore, "there is one stray dog a day." To read the books, or to visit with Quezal?

237 Sound Beach Avenue, Old Greenwich, Connecticut 06870; Tel. 203-637-5106. Hours: Monday–Saturday, 9:00 A.M.–6:00 P.M.; Thursdays, 9:00 A.M.–8:00 P.M.

THE GREENS FARMS BOOKSTORE

WESTPORT CONNECTICUT

There is a green-carpeted sidewalk outside the store which follows through green double-doors into the interior. The walls are green and white and there is a structure called the Great Green Gazebo—filled with hanging plants and other growing things—in the center of the store. Immediately, there is a sense of pleasant, clean efficiency. A plant store? No, a secret garden of books.

Founded in 1973 by Paul W. Hush, and operated by him and his wife, Joanne, the Greens Farms Bookstore is already one of the finest in the Westport area and is located away from the downtown area for those customers who prefer not to combat the city crowds and traffic.

One of the most attractive aspects of the Greens Farms, aside from its decor, is its discount policy: 20 percent off the retail price of any hardcover book in the store. The chance of snapping up a bargain influences people to buy hardcover books without waiting for the paperback to come out. And when they are in the store, they browse and pick up other merchandise: the store sells reproductions of museum sculptures, stained-glass medallions, handcrafted pottery, antiques, and dollhouse furniture. There is also a large paperback section.

Greens Farms also rents books, almost exclusively best sellers. Rates are ninety-five cents for the first three days and ten cents a day thereafter. Other services include a monthly newsletter, book searching, and mailing. The store accepts most major credit cards.

"I don't personally feel that books are overpriced, but many of my customers do, so we do what we can to accommodate them," says Hush. Everyone seems happy about the arrangement.

49

1254 E. Post Road, Westport, Connecticut 06880. Tel. 203-227-4151.
Hours: Monday–Saturday, 9:30 A.M.–5:30 P.M. (Thursdays, till 8:00
P.M.); Sunday, 12:00 Noon–5:00 P.M.

REMARKABLE BOOK SHOP   WESTPORT CONNECTICUT

"Westport is not a good fiction town," says Esther Kramer, owner of the Remarkable Book Shop, "so we carry a preponderance of nonfiction books, and we're well stocked with poetry, cookbooks, travel, art. We carry very few mass-market titles, but have a plentiful supply of quality trade paper titles."

Located in a 240-year-old house that is painted a bright shocking pink, the Remarkable clearly lives up to its name. It's a charming-looking store, complete with a fireplace, old floorboards, beamed ceilings, and antique furniture. Its cellar, used for storage, looks like a catacomb hewn out of rock. Outside there are book bins and stalls full of books at bargain prices which give the store a "left-bank—Connecticut-bohemia" look.

The clientele of the Remarkable are remarkable in their own right: Joanne Woodward has a charge account; Erica Jong stops in occasionally; Dustin Hoffman, Sandy Dennis, Eva LeGalliene, Sterling Hayden, June Havoc, and Bette Davis are all customers. There are also a number of writers who constantly frequent the store. "Everybody in Westport writes a book at one time or another," says Doris Sherwood, the store manager.

The ten clerks who work in the store are all well read and they get along together: the customers feel the esprit de corps and relax, as a result. Some customers will talk for hours—one might think that the Remarkable serves as an inexpensive substitute for a visit to a psychiatrist.

The only thing Esther Kramer dislikes about her business is the Christmas rush. "It's shoulder to shoulder in here," she says. Off to the catacombs!

177 Main Street, Westport, Connecticut 06880; Tel. 203-227-1000.
Hours: Monday–Saturday, 9:00 A.M.–6:00 P.M.

Books are masters who instruct us without rods or ferules, without words or anger, without bread or money. If you approach them, they are not asleep; if you seek them, they do not hide; if you blunder, they do not scold; if you are ignorant, they do not laugh at you.

RICHARD DE BURY

51

Washington, D.C.

AUDUBON BOOK SHOP **WASHINGTON
D.C.**

Imagine a beautiful old brick building that houses a bookstore. Inside, there are dark wooden shelves, polished wood floors, and oriental rugs scattered about. Think of a bitterly cold winter day. There's a fire crackling in an open hearth in the store. You pause in your browsing to sit by the fire, warming yourself. You begin to have a conversation with one of the people who work in the store or with another customer. After a while, you continue your browsing.

A scene from a movie? Not really. This is the atmosphere at the Audubon Book Shop, one of the country's most pleasant and interesting bookshops of any kind. Owned by the Audubon Naturalist Society, the Audubon Book Shop is a nonprofit organization, with all the income going to the Society to help in its attempt to educate the public in how to improve the environment.

Although the strongest concentration of books stocked at the Audubon Book Shop is on ornithology, there are thousands of books on nature, animals, conservation, ecology, and the environment as well. The shop also carries records, field guides, stationery, prints, and other gift items. The store's print collection is remarkable in its wide number of lithographs and prints of natural history subjects done by well-known nature artists. The environmental education section is superb and is well known by teachers all over the country. Special educational discounts are given to school orders.

The shop has sponsored various activities in the past—

author autograph parties, readings for children, and even lectures—and expects to continue them from time to time. The Society itself is an integral part of the shop and offers a lecture series at the Smithsonian Institution, in addition to many nature trips. Although the staff has not yet finished compiling a catalog, all mail-order requests are answered by a personal letter informing the customer of what the store has in stock on a specific subject. The shop sells primarily new books, such as Dillon Ripley's magnificent volume, *Rails of the World*, but is also developing a used-book section for "serious birders," in which as many out-of-print books as possible will be kept in stock.

One of the Audubon Book Shop's most valuable assets is the enthusiasm and dedication of its staff, one of whom says: "I could not hope for a better job. The customers are delightful and are always overwhelmed by the shop. I've learned quickly that the preparation of a book in natural history is a long process and that we are the most important link—of author to reader—in that process."

1621 Wisconsin Avenue, N.W., Washington, D.C. 20007; Tel. 202-337-6062 or 338-1972. Hours: Monday–Saturday, 10:00 A.M.–5:30 P.M.

DISCOUNT BOOKS   WASHINGTON D.C.

This twenty-seven-year-old family business was founded by Bob Bialek, and is now operated by Michael Bialek, although Bob still keeps his hand in. The shop has one hundred employees and three stores, with the DuPont Circle store the best known.

It's hard to tell how many books are in stock, but an attempt is being made to computerize inventory for the first time. The hope is that the computer will be able to determine accurately the quantity of the stock, now estimated at somewhere between seventy-five and one hundred thousand books when fully stocked. And when the store is at the full-stock level, Discount competes with any store in the D.C. area.

Discount maintains a large inventory. It sells best sellers at 20 percent off and tries to offer more books for less. The shop has had autograph parties—for Buckminster Fuller and, although he would not allow them to announce it, Alex Haley. A mailing list is in process of being compiled, and the shop is connected with the Discount Record store, right next door. Things seem a bit chaotic. It's an "on-the-edge" kind of feeling. But it's real. Kevin Lewis, the manager, has been a bookaholic all his life. "I have an odd memory," he says. "I can forget everything else, but I don't forget books!"

The layout of the store has been growing almost organically. There's just room after room filled with books, plus the upstairs. "We spent a good deal of money and had plans made up, because there weren't any," says Kevin. "Then we knocked down a wall because we were going to build, and discovered all sorts of wiring and pipes inside the wall—so we put the wall back."

The philosophy of Discount Books, espoused by young Lewis, is "If it's good, we'll carry it." This pursuit of excellence got the store into some trouble several years ago—with overstocking of fine, beautiful books that sold slowly—but now there's a bit more control. However, if the poet/clerk on staff wants to buy five hundred copies of an esoteric book, he may be permitted to do so if he believes in it and can rationalize why it will sell. Books sometimes sell at Discount that do nothing elsewhere, and best sellers sometimes come in to the store and stagnate.

"We're a screwier than usual establishment," Lewis says. "I look at *Publisher's Weekly*'s best-seller list, and laugh. We have our own list."

The shop is large and rambling, and funky.

It's a melting pot, just like the community it serves.

Discount Books, 1340 Connecticut Ave. N.W., Washington, D.C. 20036; Tel. 202-785-1133. Hours: Monday–Saturday, 10:00 A.M.– 9:00 P.M.; Sunday, 12:00 Noon–5:00 P.M.

FOLIO BOOKS

WASHINGTON D.C.

Five employees oversee the stock of general classification books at the Folio. It is owned by Inga Shirer (daughter of William L. Shirer, the author of *The Rise and Fall of the Third Reich*), Fiona Rust, and Andrea Wyatt. The shop was founded in the spring of 1975, closed for that summer, then officially opened in September of that year. The emphasis here is on poetry, and the emphasis appears to be a heavy one, with poetry readings aplenty. Doug Lang, who manages the shop, says, "We've had the best readings series in the East, outside of New York." In three series, meeting once every two or three weeks since January of 1976, there have been more than forty readings. Because of the store's small size, readings tend to the intimate, with 50 or 60 people in attendance. John Ashbery drew 150, with another 50 turned away. Each reading features an out-of-town poet reading with a local poet. Wine and soft drinks are served, and a one-dollar admission charge is levied. The poets are paid expenses and a small fee. Lang explains that "audiences are very responsive, though they've gotten a bit tougher as time goes on. There's a hard core of regulars, some fifteen or twenty, and the rest are a constant turnover, coming from Baltimore, Virginia, and even from New York." The store is applying to the government for a National Endowment matching fund grant to pay more to its poets.

Recently the shop has been donating books to the Lorton Reformatory through the Martin Luther King Library. Prisoners request everything from Freud to Peanuts!

When the shop first tried to open, it was closed down because of a zoning problem. The building had been occupied by Buffalo Bill's All-Night Cafeteria, which had attracted many undesirables and had caused the community to zone out commercial establishments. An art gallery that showed but did not sell followed, but the local community backed the bookstore, and through community pressure, the area was rezoned and the store was permitted to open. Lang says that "in many ways, the community helped to create the bookstore."

2000 P Street, N.W., Washington, D.C. 20036; Tel. 202-785-1304. Hours: Monday–Friday, 10:00 A.M.–7:00 P.M.; Saturday, 10:00 A.M.–6:00 P.M.

Old books, as you well know, are books of the world's youth, and new books are fruits of its age.
OLIVER WENDELL HOLMES

KRAMER BOOKS & AFTERWORDS CAFÉ

WASHINGTON D.C.

Munch on quiche as you thumb through the latest best seller. Sip an aperitif as you look over a foreign periodical. Or slowly sip your cappuccino as you read the morning paper, with a fresh croissant for sustenance.

William Kramer, the young owner of several bookstores in and around Washington, recently launched a delightful innovation he calls Kramer Books & Afterwords. Opened on October 1, 1976, the shop is a true integration of bookstore and café of the European sort. Kramer took a vacation in Spain in 1971 and was enchanted by the Spanish *tascas*, where people go for leisurely snacks and conversation before moving on for a late-night dinner. No one is rushed, the food and drink are light, and the talk is friendly. Kramer wondered why there weren't such places in the United States. Then, being the heir to Sydney Kramer Books, he began to connect the two ideas: a combination bookstore and café. Kramer Books & Afterwords is the serendipitous result.

Located near Washington's busy and fashionable DuPont Circle, right near the new stop of the Washington Metro, Kramer Books & Afterwords has become a place to go when you've time to spend, to treat yourself to a most pleasant and relaxing morning, afternoon, or evening. They open early each morning; go in and browse through the bookracks, take your choice to a cheerful table, and look through it as you eat a continental breakfast.

Stay for lunch: the menu includes light but excellent foods—quiche, soup of the day, various salads, and pâtés and cheeses. Dinner features a daily special. There's an excellent dessert menu, a variety of coffees, teas, and soft drinks. And there's a complete bar, which features aperitifs, brandies, and a well-stocked wine cellar.

Lest this sound more like a café than a bookstore, here are some facts about the print part of the establishment. Kramer Books & Afterwords has about eight thousand titles currently in stock. They're all new books, in all categories: fiction and nonfiction, hardbound as well as paper. The emphasis is on paperbacks. It's a good general book collection, and should you not find what you want, the management will special-order titles, either directly from the publishers or from the inventories of the other Kramer bookstores, which means that they can get most titles fairly quickly. Incidentally, all clothbound bestsellers are sold at a 15 percent discount.

The store also carries an assortment of more than one hundred foreign and domestic newspapers and magazines. It accepts most credit cards.

The reading matter is in the front of the airy, wood-paneled store; in the back is the charming, two-level café, which spills over onto the sidewalk in warm weather. The ambience is warm and friendly, and totally unhurried.

But how does it all work? In the most relaxed manner possible. Wander in, look through the books, and choose one that strikes your fancy. Bring it over to a table and examine it at your lesiure while you sip or eat, with classical music playing softly in the background. The management smilingly hopes you won't drip on the pages, but for those of us who habitually read at the table, that skill is just second nature.

Kramer Books & Afterwords likes parties and holds about one a month. Often they're for local authors or autographing sessions. Sunday brunch is a major event. The store draws many Washingtonians as its steady customers, so at any time you're liable to find someone of interest there, browsing or chatting.

You can sit alone at a corner table and really read your book, but many visitors to this shop absorb congeniality from the atmosphere, and there are often intra-table conversations centering on the book or books someone is reading. Which means that Kramer has been successful, for his stated goal is "to make a congenial, relaxed bookstore that can be a neighborhood place for people who are interested in books. It's the most civilized, entertaining way to spend an evening I can imagine."

It is, indeed.

1517 Connecticut Avenue, N.W., Washington, D.C. 20036; Tel. 202-387-1400. Hours: Monday–Thursday, 8:00 A.M. to midnight; Friday, 8:00 A.M.–2:00 A.M.; Saturday, 10:00 A.M.–2:00 A.M.; Sunday, 10:00 A.M. to midnight.

There is a kind of physiognomy in the titles of books no less than in the faces of men, by which a skilled observer will know as well what to expect from the one as the other.

JOSEPH BUTLER

THE SAVILE BOOKSHOP

Founded over three decades ago by a very urbane gentleman, Donald Downs, who saw the possibilities in the slum that was then Georgetown, renovated some buildings, and started a bookstore in them, the Savile has become one of the most delightful bookshops in the country: fifteen rooms of treasures; a staff of twenty civilized, literate, and capable people; and hundreds of thousands of books—all housed in what is now a typically beautiful Georgetown shop on a pretty, tree-lined street.

Now owned by Mr. and Mrs. Wallace Kuralt, who have developed other bookstores (a chain called the Intimate Bookshops), the Savile caters to the Georgetown government and diplomatic crowd—Secret Service men browse next to Arabian sheiks, all within a bookshelf's distance from the elegantly dressed wife of a senator.

The Savile is a general bookstore and it's possible to find almost any kind of book in stock. The shop specializes in children's books and has one of the biggest and best collections in all of Washington. Paperbacks, including many mass-market books, are also featured. The hardcover stock seems somewhat heavy in scholarly works but is really excellent. The *Christian Science Monitor* dubbed the Savile "one of the best-stocked bookshops in the world," and *Look* stated that the Savile was "to other Washington bookstores what the stuffed Library of Congress is to a village library."

Wallace Kuralt claims that his shop is as good as it is because he listens to the criticisms of his customers. "They realize that it's a remarkable shop, and they want to see more. We're grateful to them, and we expect to continue to grow and improve."

The Savile Bookshop, Washington, D.C.

3236 P Street, N.W., Washington, D.C. 20007; Tel. 202-338-3321. Hours: Monday–Saturday, 10:00 A.M.–10:00 P.M.; Sunday, 12:00 Noon–6:00 P.M.

YES!   WASHINGTON D.C.

Tucked away in a row of brightly colored townhouses in the picturesque Georgetown section of Washington, D.C., is *Yes!*, a lovely bookstore where the environment is appropriately conducive and symbiotic to the spiritual and philosophical subjects of the books on display. Customers, with interests ranging from astral projection to sacred geometry and yoga, can shop in a nirvana of soft blue carpets, delicate leafy yucca plants, and batik-appointed walls—all illuminated by the sun through a dramatic skylight. On winter days there is the welcome backdrop of a large, brick fireplace. *Yes!* frequenters also have the unusual opportunity of inside or al fresco dining in a superb health food and vegetarian restaurant adjacent to the bookstore and run by the same company.

Founded in 1972 by petite, energetic Cris Popenoe and her husband, Oliver, *Yes!* has become one of the foremost counter-culture bookstores in the nation. The emphasis is hardly on the word "counter," however. *Yes!* focuses on the general category of what might once have been referred to as Bohemian but is today almost considered mainstream reading: mythology, the occult, nutrition, popular anthropology, self-help, "strange gods," and other philosophical, religious, and mystical topics. The store does not cater to the "lunatic fringe," however, as Cris will quickly point out: there are no sections on witchcraft, LSD, or sadomasochism, for example.

Yes! maintains approximately 15,000 volumes and is fast establishing an international reputation as a specialist in many spiritual fields: the Jung Foundation, among others, considers

62

Yes! to have the most complete and finest selection of books in its field and is continuously placing orders there for obscure or hard-to-find works.

A children's book section features a variety of selections that have a spiritual tone. There is even a comprehensive array of books about King Arthur and the Holy Grail and entire sections dealing with the works of Krishnamurti, Gurdjieff, Confucius, Edgar Cayce, Wilhelm Reich, et al.

Because a large amount of *Yes!* books deal with some form of self-help, Cris decided to publish a catalog, *Books for Inner Development*, highlighting the bookstore's remarkable selection of specialized reading material. More than just a compendium of eight thousand book titles, however, *Books for Inner Development* is to be savored slowly: each title is accompanied by a thoughtful appraisal. Beautiful illustrations and quotations taken from some of the books are spread throughout. The catalog, with an initial press run of twenty-five thousand copies, has been successfully distributed by Random House in the United States and Canada. The *Los Angeles Times* labeled it "the most useful guide to the literature, old and new, of the consciousness revolution yet produced." Inspired by the huge success of *Books for Inner Development* in 1977, *Yes!* published *Wellness* (which is also distributed by Random House), a catalog that lists books which deal with all types of holistic healing. There are sections on anatomy and physiology, "body work" (massage, tai chi chuan, yoga, etc.), color and aura, cookbooks, herbs, natural childbirth, nutrition, oriental medicine, and even death.

During 1977, *Yes!* sales from the bookstore totaled $535,565, up 25 percent over 1976, making it one of the most prosperous privately owned bookstores in the Washington, D.C., area. Much of the *Yes!* success must be attributed to Cris Popenoe's concern about the selection of books for her unique store and the treatment of her customers. She manages with a sincere and brilliant blend of interest in people and business acumen.

63

"I have two feelings about books," says Cris, sitting cross-legged on a natural wood bench. "On the one hand, I really like the way they can give you clues to your development, directions to go, things to do. On the other hand, they can be a crutch—people read and read, and never develop themselves. They're trapped by words." She continues, "There are some books I feel better about carrying than others, people have to be guided somewhat. I approach each person as an individual; there are things that can be dangerous and bad. We try to be as much service to the customer as possible. We have come along by not trying to convert customers to our own path, but by remaining open to others, whatever path they are on and wherever they are on it."

Cris stresses that all the bookstore employees are as helpful as possible to the customers. Everyone who works at *Yes!* has some previous knowledge—or gains knowledge quickly—of the diverse subject matter of the merchandise. In hiring employees Cris tries to make sure they're doing what they want to be doing—selling mystical and self-help books—and not taking the job as a stopgap interlude, collecting a temporary paycheck. Each person is responsible for an area or section of the store, including Cris, who maintains all of the books about India, and this has a great effect on the scope and value of all the sections. Bookstore personnel all become specialists in their fields of responsibility, learning which are the most estimable works in the field, how and where to order them, which titles are needed and which to be avoided as too frivolous or unhelpful. Cris has an M.A. in Latin American studies, with a concentration in archaeology, which has become one of the store's specialties: "It sells, real well," she states. Her other personal interests lie in Taoism, Buddhism, Gurdjieff, and Sufism, all of which she has been studying for a "long time."

The services at *Yes!* go beyond the selling of books or the dispensing of food. Having trouble with your astrological chart? *Yes!* employees may assist you in casting it. The staff is extremely prompt in processing customers' mail-order requests. All books are mailed the same day the order is received. Two full-time employees are solely responsible for mail orders. If a customer requests a particular title or type of book in a field they do not carry, they will order it from anywhere in the world to fill the request. *Yes!* staff members also often do research and prepare reading lists for customers.

Currently, the most popular books at *Yes!* deal with holistic healing, mythology, Sufism, and Christianity. In addition to selling new, used, and remaindered books (all clearly marked with labels to differentiate them), *Yes!* stocks records of Eastern music and spiritual themes, art reproductions, incense, and note cards. The *Yes!* Educational Society sponsors a series of lectures and workshops every weekend on topics as varied as those on its bookshelves. During 1977 and 1978, fifty lectures and workshops were offered by the Society, headed by such leading instructors as Shlomo Carlebach, Ram Dess, and Dr. Norman Shealy.

Cris's concept of *Yes!* is to maintain a store and business which exists to provide goods and services to the public honestly, efficiently, and profitably. According to Cris, "If someone is buying five different books on meditation, we tell them: 'Hey, you don't need all these!' " Naturally, this honest and forthright approach builds enormous customer loyalty, and this satisfaction is one of the major keys to the *Yes!* success.

Yes! refuses to say *no!* and rest on its past accomplishments. It recently opened a new "Natural Living Center" a block away, with a whole food shop, a natural cosmetics shop and an herb shop. Efforts are currently underway to start a holistic health center. And, in addition to the catalogs, *Yes!* will soon begin publishing a small number of titles in fields that have been overlooked.

Yes! customers are educated, serious, and eager to learn.

They enjoy talking with the knowledgeable *Yes!* employees and dining in the excellent restaurant. Some government officials and Washington celebrities—such as Nicholas Johnson—have recently "discovered" *Yes!*, although it is not yet displacing Sans Souci as the capital's gathering place for conversations of political intrigue.

Everything about the *Yes!* enterprise is friendly and personal. Oliver ("Ollie") Popenoe even carries this flavor through to his folksy annual report. A recent example begins, "We're a little late getting this report out this year. Planting season caught up with me and took some priority for my time." Not a typical annual report and not a typical bookstore. And yet this rapport with people and plants, things holy and natural, permeates and makes the *Yes!* philosophy of bookselling a triumph in ways both practical and sublime.

1035 31st St., N.W., Washington, D.C. 20007; Tel. 202-338-7874.
Hours: Seven days a week, 10:00 A.M.–7:00 P.M.; Thursdays, till 9:00
P.M.

People seldom read a book that is given to them.
The way to spread a work is to sell it at a low price.
                                                    SAMUEL JOHNSON

Florida

SANDY BOOK STORE

Clearwater, located on the Gulf coast of Florida, is home to roughly 78,000 people. On a downtown corner of the city is the Sandy Book Store, which is run with a philosophy that tries to attract most of the local and visiting book-buying public.

The store stocks twenty thousand books on all subjects, fiction and nonfiction, paperback as well as hardbound. All titles are new; no used books are carried. The bookstore is kept current, with "dead stock" returned to the publishers twice a year to make room for newer or more popular titles.

There is a large section of nonbook items, as well: greeting cards, stationery, party goods, candles, photo albums, scrapbooks, home office supplies, small gifts, maps, posters, and a changing stock of humorous gifts. (During the T-shirt craze, the store carried little shirts for dogs of all sizes—with inscriptions, naturally.)

Fred C. Korosy owns the Sandy Book Store, and his aim is to specialize in service. He special orders books for customers for a slight charge. All purchases are cheerfully gift-wrapped, if so desired, at no charge.

Customers may order their own imprints on stationery, Christmas cards, wedding invitations, napkins and matches, and anything else one might want to bear his name or initials.

Sandy Book Store holds an annual sale in January, covering all of its merchandise. There are special sales almost every month, on imprinted stationery and closeouts. Customers can be placed on the store's mailing list on request.

One of the most pleasurable features of the Sandy Book Store is its roominess. This is noticeable before you even enter the store. Located on a corner in downtown Clearwater, the store has a large parking lot at the rear with space for seventy cars.

Inside, the store has a lounge area where customers can sit and browse. There are also tables and chairs where customers can examine, at leisure, the many sample books for imprinted or engraved stationery or Christmas cards.

If all of this sounds a bit unusual for a bookstore, some of the reason comes from the fact that Sandy Book Store was professionally designed, by Frank Morris, AIA, of Clearwater. He developed the separate areas, the spacious feeling, the displays which show most of the books face out, rather than spine out, so the customer can really see what books are available. The end result is a large, well-stocked bookstore in which it is a delight to browse and shop.

530 Drew Street, Clearwater, Florida 33515; Tel. 813-446-4023 and 4024. Hours: Monday–Saturday, 9:00 A.M.–5:30 P.M.

HASLAM'S   ST. PETERSBURG
FLORIDA

One of the great things about Haslam's is that despite the fact that it is an enormous bookstore dealing in both new and used books, the owner, Charles Haslam, seems to know the location of each and every volume. Originally established forty-five years ago by his parents, the business now includes his wife (co-owner and expert on children's literature), their son-in-law (assistant manager) and daughter. It takes twenty-two employees to handle the 250,000 volumes displayed in 17,000 square feet of space.

Having located in a community of many retirees as well as several colleges—a prime area for people who like, want, or need to read—Haslam has established himself as *the* bookman

68

in the Tampa-St. Petersburg area and his store as the best in all of Florida. His reputation spans forty years, and he is constantly consulted on books old and new; a television program, "Wonderful World of Books," has been his special feature for years in addition to regular appearances on local television talk-shows. Haslam was elected president of the American Booksellers Association in May 1978 and has traveled extensively in the U.S. and around the world promoting the book business.

Haslam's is a general bookstore and is also known for its excellent sections of religious books, bibles, and used books of every kind. It has a special used paperback feature: bring one and take one for five cents. Hundreds of books are brought in on a daily basis and are exchanged this way. *Haslam's Too*, a recent expansion of 5,000 square feet, is allotted to bargains and remainders.

In spite of all the expansions and personal achievements, Haslam's greatest joy is still "getting the right book to the right customer." With both parking lots frequently jammed, Charles Haslam proclaims, "This is Florida's greatest rainy-day attraction!"

2025 Central Avenue, St. Petersburg, Florida 33713; Tel. 813-822-8616. Hours: Monday–Saturday, 9:00 A.M.–5:30 P.M.; Friday, 9:00 A.M.–9:00 P.M.

Georgia

RICH'S

ATLANTA
GEORGIA

Rich's department store is one of the most famous, largest, and oldest in the South, dating back from the days when the city was burnt to ashes by General Sherman and his troops. It has eight book departments and is well known for its large selections of books on cookery, religion, and diet, as well as best sellers and gift books.

Rich's book-buyer, Faith Brunson, is witty and vivacious. "I never read a book before I buy it," she jokes. Rich's philosophy of bookselling includes doing nothing that will offend a customer and everything that will please him. "The customer is always right," says Ms. Brunson. "That may sound like a cliché, but we really believe it." When *The Joy of Sex* was on every best-seller list in the country, Rich's received a number of requests for it. The store was afraid that the book might disturb some customers, who might inadvertently pick it up without knowing its content. On the other hand, however, customers who did want the book would be upset if the store *didn't* carry it. The solution: copies were kept in the utility room for anyone who wanted to look through the book or buy it; that room is now laughingly referred to as their "pornographic parlor."

Rich's enjoys pleasing its customers, even if it means ordering five paperbacks to get one copy for someone who wants it. The store holds celebrity teas, luncheons, and dinners, with talks by well-known Southern writers. It has also arranged exhibits of the works of such Georgia writers as Joel Chandler Harris and Sidney Lanier.

One of Rich's best-selling books of late is *Why Not the Best?*, by a fellow state resident, Jimmy Carter.

45 Broad Street, Atlanta, Georgia 30302; Tel. 404-586-2349. Hours: Monday–Saturday, 10:00 A.M.–6:00 P.M.

I cannot imagine a pleasanter old age than one spent in the not too remote country where I could reread and annotate my favorite books.

ANDRÉ MAUROIS

71

Hawaii

BOOK GALLERIES INC.

**HILO
HAWAII**

The next time you are vacationing in this island paradise or want to know more about the fiftieth state, stop in or write to one of the Book Galleries, two general bookstores that also happen to have the most extensive collections of Hawaiiana in the world. There are thirty-five thousand books in the main store, which is housed in an old wooden frame building (built in 1934) that is typical of downtown Hilo. A new branch store, conveniently located in the Kaikoo Mall, provides the same type of books.

Any time a new book on Hawaii comes out, owners Martin and Judy Beeman have an autographing party for the author, but the main thrust of their store is to give good service to their customers. They do a great deal of special ordering and will do book searching for out-of-print books.

Martin Beeman succinctly explains how he runs his shop: "We supply good reading material to the public."

211 Kinoole St., Hilo, Hawaii 96720; Tel. 808-935-3186. Hours: Monday–Saturday, 9:00 A.M.–5:00 P.M. Kaikoo Mall, Hilo, Hawaii 96720; Tel. 808-935-2447. Hours: Monday–Saturday, 9:00 A.M.–9:00 P.M.; Sunday, 10:00 A.M.–3:00 P.M.

No arts; no letters; no society.

THOMAS HOBBES

Idaho

THE BOOK SHOP

BOISE
IDAHO

What makes a memorable bookstore? In some cases, it may be the vastness of the stock. Or it may be the excellent book collection which a given store specializes in. Or the uniqueness of the store's layout and design.

In the case of the Book Shop, it is the extraordinary degree of personal service which the staff regularly provides for its clientele. And they really are remarkable, so much so that the store has gained a reputation among the often jaded publishers' representatives, who spend their working days visiting bookstores throughout the country, as one of the best "personal" bookstores extant.

The Book Shop keeps detailed records on the preferences and interests of its customers. The staff notifies a customer when his (or her) favorite author comes out with a new book. They'll also telephone a customer, or write him a short note, to describe newly acquired books in which they think he might be interested. They do book searches, even tracking down titles by obscure publishers. The enthusiasm of the salespeople is genuine; each of them is a confirmed book lover, and they convey their enjoyment and fascination about books each time they help a customer with a request.

The Book Shop had to become special in order to survive. Boise has fewer than 100,000 residents, yet boasts eight different bookstores. One of them, like the Book Shop, is a general bookstore. But the Book Shop does a brisk business. It carries all new titles, and maintains a strong backlist, plus a large stock of used books.

Founded in 1875 by James A. Pinney, a former mayor of the then young city, the Book Shop was for years home to an assorted collection of rocks and minerals ("Souvenir of Boise, Idaho") and a musty, dusty jumble of assorted books. Two Boise businessmen, Tom Fisher and Harry Schuppel, bought the store in 1951 and hired Nancy Stringfellow to manage it, and under her direction the store took on its current guise. Jean Wilson, a longtime customer, went to work in the shop during the 1962 Christmas season, and stayed on to become co-owner with Mr. Schuppel in 1973. As the store continued to grow, it needed more space, and recently moved into its current home in a newly restored building originally built in the city's pioneer days. In the center of downtown Boise, it maintains a bit of the serenity of the past, with its rough, original brick walls, antique sales desk, even a gazebo.

The new store has some innovations. There is a children's section, with scaled down furniture, where kids can browse without adult interference.

The Book Shop features a section on Western Americana which is considered to be one of the best of its kind. It was started by Mrs. Stringfellow, a nationally recognized authority in the field who, though retired, still acts as the store's consultant on Western Americana and on rare books. The store ships books to collectors all over the world.

If you enjoy buying books by mail, the store will service your order as it does for customers throughout the world. But if you can, stop in. It's the kind of place where you'll want to meet the people.

908 Main Street; Boise, Idaho; Tel. 208-342-2659; Hours: Monday–Friday, 8:30 A.M.–5:30 P.M.; Saturday, 9:30 A.M.–5:30 P.M.

In reality, every reader, as he reads, is the reader of himself.
MARCEL PROUST

THE BOOKSELLER

Hidden away in the center of mountainous northern Idaho and within viewing distance of beautiful Lake Coeur d'Alene, the Bookseller is easily recognized from the street by the distinctive and handsome stained-glass hanging sign. It gives the store a Victorian atmosphere. Inside, the browser will find an enormous stock of books on all subjects, with an emphasis on Western Americana and "back-to-the-land" books, which are much in demand by what the store's owners humorously but astutely call their "pragmatic country and sophisticated urban-escapee" customers. The stock carried by the Bookseller is huge, considering the size of the local territory and the sparse population.

Located in the center of the store is always a sale table containing some interesting bargains—remainders, slightly worn new books, or close-outs. Other sales are announced by mail, and customers can be included on the mailing list simply by sending their names and addresses to the store. The Bookseller accepts Visa credit cards and Master Charge.

Owners Steve and Janis Meyer state: "Our philosophy of bookselling is to carry books without letting our bias interfere with stock selection. And if we don't have a book, we'll gladly order it."

423 Sherman Avenue, Coeur d'Alene, Idaho 83814; Tel. 208-664-8811. Hours: Monday–Saturday, 9:30 A.M.–5:30 P.M.

*There is no book so bad but
something valuable may be derived from it.*

PLINY

Illinois

STUART BRENT   **CHICAGO**
ILLINOIS

There are few bookstores in the United States that are so inexorably identified with their owners as is Stuart Brent's. Brent is a highly educated, totally outspoken, passionate book lover and seller, who is also a writer, father, and Chicago literary light. He's also delightfully eccentric about what books he will and will not carry in his store, which is located on Chicago's "Magnificent Mile." Brent vows that he only stocks "books that I believe in—it can't be any other way!"

Brent's store is almost opulent: high ceilings, beautiful wood shelves, polished hardwood floors, classical music playing softly on an unseen hi-fi, a table and comfortable chairs at the back for browsing. There is a good selection of current hardback books, especially in the areas of art, politics, and philosophy, but Brent's specialty is what is unquestionably the most extensive selection of books on psychology, psychoanalysis, and psychiatry in the country. The store is thus a favorite haunt of Chicago's analysts, many of whom have their offices in the same neighborhood. A special catalog covering this category is available free of charge to anyone who writes for it.

The basement of the store, reached by a circular stairway, contains thousands of paperbacks and one of the best children's sections in the city of Chicago.

Brent's philosophy of bookselling has affected his way of life in that he believes that being surrounded by books has a great influence on people who work in bookstores. Therefore, he has his wife working with him, and each of his eight children has worked in the store at one time or another.

"A bookstore is a sacred place," says Brent. "It's a place of learning and mystery and life. What better thing to do than browse in a good bookstore?"

670 N. Michigan Avenue, Chicago, Illinois 60611; Tel. 312-337-6357. Hours: Monday–Friday, 9:00 A.M.–7:00 P.M.; Saturday, 9:00 A.M.– 6:00 P.M.; Sunday, 12:00 Noon–5:00 P.M.

BARBARA'S BOOKSTORE
CHICAGO ILLINOIS

Chicago's Old Town is the city's answer to New York's Greenwich Village: a section of small shops, cafés, and boutiques where many of the residents are writers, artists, and craftspeople of all kinds and varieties, amateur and professional. Located on Wells Street, the principal thoroughfare of Old Town, which has of late taken on a slightly honky-tonk atmosphere, is Barbara's Bookstore, one of the best literary emporiums in the Windy City. Formerly owned by Barbara Siegel, a former publicity director of several publishing firms, the store combines old-fashioned service with very modern functional features, such as movable shelves and cases and excellent lighting. Today the store is owned and operated by Don Barliant.

Although it is a general bookstore with new hardcover and paperback books, Barbara's is known for its superb selection of drama and film books, and poetry and fiction, especially the small press variety.

The store occasionally holds autographing parties for local notables such as Studs Terkel or Henry Rago, and also conducts poetry readings by well-known poets such as Lawrence Ferlinghetti and Paul Carroll.

Special orders are cheerfully accepted, and browsing is not

only encouraged, it is expected and desired.

1434 N. Wells St., Chicago, Illinois 60610; Tel. 312-642-5044. Hours: Seven days a week, 11:00 A.M. to 10:00 P.M.

GREAT EXPECTATIONS

EVANSTON ILLINOIS

Samuel Johnson's idea of combining good books with good conversation is realized in Great Expectations, a bookstore which is located near the campus of Northwestern University. Here, students meet, listen to Bach's Goldberg Variations on the phonograph, browse through an excellent humanities section, and have a cup of coffee while waiting for the next class to start. There is a chess table, a bulletin board crammed full of pertinent notices, and other tables where students work out math problems, study for language exams, or plan their term's work. All the time there is talk, debate, and conversation.

In all, the store has about twenty thousand books, including numerous used books, and the emphasis is on philosophy, literature, and politics. The Northwestern University philosophy club holds meetings there which usually go late into the night. It all seems a natural part of Great Expectations.

Founded by Bob Geary, it is now owned by Truman T. Metzel, who explained the meaning of the store's name: "Not only did the original owner have a great liking for Dickens's classic, but he felt that browsing for books should be carried on in an atmosphere of expectancy of new ideas. We've attempted to continue to encourage that anticipation."

911 Foster St., Evanston, Illinois 60201; Tel. 312-864-3881. Hours: Monday–Friday, 10:00 A.M.–7:00 P.M., Saturday, 10:00 A.M.–6:00 P.M.

PARK RIDGE
BOOK STORE

PARK RIDGE
ILLINOIS

Norman G. and Lucille H. Wolcott describe the Park Ridge Book Store as "a typical small-town store." Perhaps so, but they said something else, too, that caught our interest. When we asked about their philosophy as booksellers, their reply was: "To give customers the best service of which we are capable at a price which is harmonious with the times. We try to match the book with the customer, to give him something with which he is pleased and which will bring him back to our store a satisfied customer."

Founded in April of 1969, the store now has four employees; boasts a stock of some twenty thousand books, covering general hardbound books, quality paperbacks, and mass-market paperbacks; and is still growing.

The store is built on a strong foundation of customer service. The staff fills special orders for book lovers, and there are periodic seasonal sales. When the opportunity presents itself, the store holds author autograph parties.

In addition to books, the stock includes greeting cards, jigsaw puzzles, wooden toys, backgammon, chess, and other games. The store honors Master Charge and a local credit card, Park Ridge Blue Card. And if you visit Park Ridge in August, you can benefit from their old-fashioned sidewalk sale—tables of bargains are set up in front of the store and become a browser's delight.

25 S. Prospect Avenue, Park Ridge, Illinois 60068; Tel. 312-825-4901. Hours: Monday–Saturday, 9:30 A.M.–5:30 P.M.; Thursdays, 9:30 A.M.–9:00 P.M.

Books are a finer world within the world.
ALEXANDER SMITH

Iowa

THE BOOK STORE, INC.   DES MOINES
                                           IOWA

"If a town is bad for books, if not many books are sold there,
then they simply don't have a good bookstore in that town,"
said the late Ray W. Vanderhoef, a founder of the Book Store.
"It's not that the populace is necessarily illiterate." Owner Ben
Gibson agrees with this philosophy, and they run their store
accordingly—stocking it with the best, most advanced, and
practical literary books on the market.

The Book Store is one of the most complete literary emporiums in the state of Iowa, and the stock consists of a large
representative sampling of general books, both hardbound and
paperback.

Aside from the books that it sells to the citizens of Des
Moines and nearby towns, people drive from miles around to
shop there. The Book Store carries a large stock of books on the
local areas, state and cities.

Because of the quantity and quality of its books, the Book
Store does a large amount of its trade with businesses, public
and private schools, and church libraries in the area. It has also
established a lending-library situation for one corporation,
where, as a fringe benefit, employees can get books free of
charge from the company. The Book Store selected the
books—of high literary quality—and the corporation bought
2,500 titles.

*308 6th Ave., Des Moines, Iowa 50309; Tel. 515-288-7267. Hours:
Monday–Friday, 9:30 A.M.–5:30 P.M.; Saturday 9:30 A.M.–4:00 P.M.*

Kansas

TREASURE CHEST BOOK SHOP

GREAT BEND KANSAS

If you find yourself in Great Bend, in central Kansas on the Arkansas River, make it a point to stop in and say hello to Wynona Gordon, owner of the Treasure Chest Book Shop. Founded in 1971, it now boasts some three thousand paperback titles and three hundred clothbound books. The store is run by the owner and two part-time helpers, and the general flavor of this shop is one of personal service. Though it is modest in size, the quality of books is quite high. The assortment of titles is general in nature, but there is an area of specialization—cookbooks.

If Wynona doesn't have a particular book that you're after, she'll be happy to order it, and if you live in the area, keep an eye out for her semiannual book sales.

Unfortunately, the Treasure Chest Book Shop doesn't have famous authors stopping by for autographing parties, as the shop is too far off the beaten path to attract such literary lights, who tend to gravitate to the large urban centers. However, occasionally a local author will produce a book, and that's when the Treasure Chest goes to town with full-flown autographing sessions.

2025 Forest, Great Bend, Kansas 67530; Tel. 316-793-9077. Hours: Monday–Saturday, 9:00 A.M.–5:30 P.M.

There are no bad books, any more than there are ugly women.

ANATOLE FRANCE

Kentucky

THE OWL AND THE PUSSYCAT

LEXINGTON KENTUCKY

This charming shop seems more like someone's home than like the thriving bookstore it is. In it you can buy a book for a really bright four-year-old, help a child who's a problem reader, or get advice on how to organize a children's book fair. The building is really an old house, and children usually sit comfortably on the floor, leafing through books, their toys scattered nearby. Customers often say that it looks like their family room.

The Owl and the Pussycat calls itself a bookshop for children. It's that, and more. The majority of its thirty thousand volumes are, indeed, books for children, and they cover many categories, many interests, and all ages. The great children's classics are there: *Rebecca of Sunnybrook Farm*, *The Tale of Peter Rabbit*, *The Wizard of Oz*. And books by the great storytellers who have been children's favorites for generations: Mark Twain, A. A. Milne, Jack London, Laura Ingalls Wilder, Isaac Bashevis Singer. The new classics are all there, too; books by the inimitable Dr. Seuss; Jean de Brunhoff's series on the delightful Babar; Lois Lenski.

There are cloth books and alphabet books for babies and toddlers; nursery rhymes from the traditional Mother Goose to an ethnically illustrated Mother Goose, and something called *Chinese Mother Goose Rhymes* which presents, in Chinese verse and English translation, beautifully illustrated rhymes, riddles, and games that Chinese mothers have traditionally taught their children.

There are books about animals, books about science, books

about children, books about growing up. Some of the books aren't even books. The history section contains "Jackdaws," a series of folders on various historic events; each folder contains a resumé of the incident, plus facsimiles of documents, letters, charts, and illustrations relating to it.

For older children, there are books by the history-makers themselves; Abba Eban's *My People*, John Fitzgerald Kennedy's *Profiles in Courage*. And, of course, there are books on science fiction, crafts and hobbies, games, art, religion. There are books for almost every child, for virtually any occasion.

In addition, The Owl and the Pussycat stocks books for adults—those that concern children; books on parenting, teaching, keeping children amused on rainy afternoons, helping children learn, teaching children to read and write before school (or in spite of it), helping disturbed children, and so on.

Debra Shine founded The Owl and the Pussycat in 1968 because she was unable to find a good source of books for her own children. Now her shop holds many special events to serve her customers. There are special lectures for students of library science (particularly students from the nearby University of Kentucky). Mrs. Shine also speaks to groups of parents and teachers about selection of books and the value of reading and provides an advisory service for groups wanting to hold book fairs in schools.

The store provides additional service for its customers. The staff will offer advice on book selection, keep a record of the interests of—and the books you've already bought for—each child on your list, and provide reading lists and advice for helping slow or reluctant readers. They promise to supply any book in print.

The store's excellent annual catalog (cost: $1.75) lists many of the books in stock by age group and author, and by subject areas. The catalog and the store's cooperative and helpful policies encourage mail-order requests, and the shop now has customers from all over the world.

83

The store carries some teaching aids, a small quantity of quality toys, UNICEF cards, posters, and mobiles for children. It accepts Master Charge and Visa credit cards.

The clientele of The Owl and the Pussycat includes, primarily, children of highly educated and motivated parents; parents of children with reading or learning problems; and librarians and libraries. Many customers are friends or relatives who want to give a book to a child and aren't sure which to choose. Debra Shine's bookselling philosophy indicates why the customers keep coming back: "I feel evangelistic about bringing books and children together. I am not interested in selling any book that will not be read by the recipient."

314 South Ashland Avenue, Lexington, Kentucky 40502; Tel. 606-266-7121. Hours: Monday–Saturday, 10:00 A.M.–5:00 P.M.

As good almost kill a man as kill a good book: who kills a man kills a reasonable creature, God's image; but he who destroys a book kills reason itself, kills the image of God, as it were, in the eye.

JOHN MILTON

Louisiana

MAPLE STREET BOOK SHOP

NEW ORLEANS LOUISIANA

In a city with more than fifty bookstores, we can still claim that this is the best bookstore in New Orleans. It has a large stock of new books on all subjects, and since it is in a university area, it features strong sections on literature and literary criticism, history, education, philosophy, and psychology. It also carries current best sellers, cookbooks, and travel books.

Owner Rhoda Faust took over the shop from her mother in 1970; before that, it had specialized in underground and leftist literature. Rhoda has made a successful effort to make the shop a comfortable place to browse, and the staff all try hard to help customers find precisely what they're searching for—or if it's unavailable, to find a viable substitute; or, as Rhoda Faust muses, "to have just been treated nicely and to have had a pleasant browse."

The management will special order, at no extra charge, any title that is in print. The shop services mail-order requests and accepts major credit cards.

The Maple Street Book Shop is located in an area that promotes browsing. It's surrounded by many small specialty stores, interspersed with small, neighborhood restaurants. And the shop itself is well organized, located in a remodeled frame house which has retained the charm of old New Orleans.

Apparently, visiting the shop becomes habit-forming. Local customers tend to drop in several times a week, and people who have moved away tend to "pop in for a visit" when they return to New Orleans—or to write to ask the store to send specific books by mail.

There are two branch stores you might also want to visit. The Maple Street Children's Book Shop (7529 Maple Street; tel. 504-861-2105) is right next door, in a spacious "house." It carries a good stock of books for children, as well as toys by Creative Playthings.

Maple Street's Garden District Book Shop is at 1454 Jackson Avenue at Prytania (504-524-5861). It carries a slightly smaller stock than its parent store, but has a good general selection, as well as a large section of children's books, books about New Orleans, and books by New Orleans writers. This branch is further downtown, in a Greek Revival townhouse dating from 1850 which stands at the edge of the city's mansion-filled Garden District.

7523 Maple Street, New Orleans, Louisiana 70118; Tel. 504-866-4916. Hours: Monday–Saturday, "around 10:00 A.M. to a little after 6:00 P.M."

BASEMENT BOOK SHOP NEW ORLEANS LOUISIANA

Founded in 1927 by Erma and Fanny Kahn, the Basement Book Shop has been owned and operated by the irrepressible Tess Mayer Crayer, grande dame of New Orleans letters, since 1931. The shop is no longer in a basement, however, but in a rickety wooden house. What will you find in Tess's domain? Thousands of books, fiction and nonfiction, with scarcely a paperback in sight. Mysteries, Gothics, books for children, and books for art connoisseurs fill the shop's cluttered, sometimes dusty, walls. "It's the worst-looking bookstore in the world," says Tess, with a touch of delightful irony. But it's also one of the most charming.

According to Tess, bookselling today is NOT like it used to be. But to see her operation, you would think that today's computerized, impersonal way of doing business was a mere illusion. The Basement Book Shop eschews credit cards; and such sure-fire moneymakers as greeting cards, posters, and stationery have never adorned the store's dusty shelves.

On a typical day, you may observe the Book Shop's owner sweeping the floor, washing the windows, or dispensing advice to her affluent clientele. "You won't believe what I do for my customers," Tess states begrudgingly. "I am their unpaid shrink. Why, I even take books home with me and let my customers pick them up after hours." And when Tess sees a book that she thinks will appeal to a special customer, she just calls him up.

There is no photo of Sinclair Lewis, even though he often visited the store. "He was an ugly man and he behaved abominably," says Tess. "I remember Faulkner," she says, with a twinkle in her eye. "He occasionally would come and sleep on my couch. He was a small, neat man, though he wore a bedraggled, tweedy suit. His big brag was that he had served in the Royal Air Force and had a silver plate in his head as a result of a war wound. One time we all had a party on a boat on Lake Pontchartrain—it was a disaster, the engine spilled oil all over, attracted all kinds of mosquitoes. I suppose that's what gave Faulkner the idea for his book, *Mosquitoes*. I believe that Faulkner is presently overrated. But Faulkner had personal charisma—he was sponsored by some powerful person, I can't remember who, some woman of prominence, and then he went to Hollywood, and after he made it big, he wouldn't talk to his old friends in New Orleans."

7221 Zimpel Street, New Orleans, Louisiana 70118; Tel. 504-861-0111. Hours: Monday–Saturday, 9:30 A.M.–5:30 P.M.

87

Maine

THE OWL AND THE TURTLE, INC.

The autumn trees of the Maine countryside are golden and scarlet. You've spent the day driving slowly, gaining pleasure at each new vista. But it's twilight, now. Time to stop for the night. You drive into the lovely little town of Camden and find a nice little motel. Or is it a bookstore?

In fact, The Owl and the Turtle is the only combination bookstore and motel that we've come across, and the odd-sounding association is surprisingly successful. Though many of the bookstore's customers are nearby residents, motel visitors are immediately lured into the bookstore—which looks more like a living room than a place of business. A Mr. Sterling Tinsley, of Rockport, arrived wet and tired one rainy night in 1974, checked into the motel, and then paid a visit to the store. He summed up his reaction to the experience in a poem:

> the owl and the turtle
>
> let wisdom stand secure
> as time unveils its path unseen
> as winter's buried seed emerges
> spring's young hope and
> summer's fruit:
>
> a taste of ripeness
> offered up in gentle hands
> warmed by many summers
> passed in thought
> and movement planted then

tended carefully
grown to bloom for me to hear
one windy rain-filled night
"step in, friend, you're welcome here."

The bookstore is divided into four rooms; a general reading room, an arts and crafts room, a children's room, and what they call a marine room. This last one contains all kinds of books on marine subjects, including all five hundred titles of Camden's International Marine Publishing Company. It also features nautical and topographical charts.

Founded and operated by the William G. Conrad family, The Owl and the Turtle holds autograph parties and works with the AAUW to provide the annual Maine Authors Series. The store issues its own Christmas catalog, and if you wish to be placed on the mailing list, just give the store your name and address. The store services many mail-order requests, and the numerous clerks provide excellent service. The store also does a great deal of special-order research for customers.

In addition to books and charts, The Owl and the Turtle sells cards and records—almost entirely classical. The shop's displays are often exceptional, so much so that the staff recently won a prize in an *American Heritage Dictionary* display contest.

The store also inspired another poem, this one dedicated to it by Dr. Bradley Dewey, of Franklin and Marshall College, Pennsylvania:

Our bookshop's sure to please
It's well supplied with tomes designed
To release that urban squeeze.

One wonders whether it's the owl or the turtle that inspires the poetic muse.

8 Bay View Street, Camden, Maine 04843; Tel. 207-236-4769. Hours: Monday–Saturday, 8:30 A.M.–5:30 P.M.; Summers, open seven days a week, 8:30 A.M.–9:00 P.M.

KENNEBUNK
BOOK PORT

KENNEBUNKPORT
MAINE

Located on the southwestern coast of Maine, the fishing village of Kennebunkport is situated near two bodies of water: the Atlantic Ocean and the Kennebunk River. It is one of the most charming and picturesque towns in all of New England—a large section of the residential area has been designated an Historic Preservation District by the National Park Service—and, appropriately, it has one of the friendliest and loveliest bookstores in the country.

The owners of the Kennebunk Book Port, Tom and Dorothy Jeglosky, opened it in 1972, after deciding to move to the town and establish roots. They tell of their adventure in their colorful Christmas card of last year:

Our own love affair with Maine is still so new that it would be presumptuous to try to explain Maine to anyone else. We can speak solely of our own experience. We were drawn here by the history, the sea, the small village where our children can walk to school, the rootedness our migratory society finds so scarce. But as we lived and worked and grew in Maine, we found ourselves caring, and being cared for, as never before . . . as if we had married into a large, very close family. This community caring is, we feel, a result of centuries of living together, dependent on one another. Dependent, yet enormously independent. Only people with such integrity could have built the serenely beautiful yet individual homes in our villages, nurtured the elms as important for our grandchildren, integrated the older people into the daily fabric of life. And over all a wit, a twinkle, a gentleness of manner that makes living in the state of mind called Maine a joyful, rewarding adventure.

The store carries a general line of books and specializes in

Kennebunk Book Port, Kennebunkport, Maine

books about Maine or by Mainers and books about the sea and sailing. The store will order any book for a customer, offers free gift-wrapping, issues gift certificates, and accepts personal checks. In many ways this is one of the most active bookstores extant, and it is continually sponsoring all manner of events: pumpkin contests at Halloween, Easter egg contests, misspelling contests, autographing parties, coloring book contests, benefits for the local museum. In addition to books, the stock includes Maine posters, Maine maps, bookmarks, bookplates, note cards, postcards, and calendars. The store also accepts Master Charge, Visa, and American Express.

The delightful old building that the bookstore is in is the oldest commercial building in Kennebunkport, built in 1775 as a warehouse for the West Indies Company and used to store rum and molasses. The Jegloskys bought the building, and when they opened the bookstore on the second floor (where it still is), were told that they were crazy, that no retail business had ever been conducted upstairs before. Tom is a genius with flowers . . . he loaded the stairs up to the entrance at the back and the deck outside with dozens of pots of flowering plants which draw even little old ladies with canes up the stairs like a magnet. One dear old soul tottered up, looked around the store in amazement, and whispered loudly to her companion, "I've seen this place from the outside for four years, but I never knew they sold books!"

In line with the store's philosophy, the Kennebunk Book Port is arranged to be a total experience; i.e., the Jegloskys have sacrificed "valuable" selling space for a comfortable old sofa and an antique Franklin stove that is always blazing on chilly days. Their resident cat, Lucifer, has quite a following; people come in asking for him; he gets fan mail; a favorite customer sends him fresh catnip each spring; and he's so friendly he'd just as soon curl up and purr on the nearest lap without so much as an introduction.

The Jegloskys have retained the architectural purity of the

old building and have built original fixtures of wood, stained to blend in. There are wide floorboards that slant in every direction; some of the original graffiti is still visible on the two-hundred-year-old beams.

Outside the entrance is a sign: "Ice cream, candy, barefeet, short hair, long hair, no hair, cats, dogs, and small dragons . . . are welcome here anytime."

Although Kennebunkport is a friendly town, most other shops have signs that say: "No ice cream, candy, barefeet, dogs, etc., etc., ad infinitum." The Jegloskys report that they have had no damage that they can remember from their policy of allowing anyone—or thing—into the store.

At Christmas they put up a decorated tree that fills their front window clear up to the peak of the roof. Covered with hundreds of Italian beelights, it's a magnificent sight from the Square on a snowy night—a scene from Dickens or a lithograph of a Victorian Christmas card.

Apple bags: The Jegloskys couldn't afford regular shopping bags when they opened, so they substituted. The bags were so successful that now they order them on a regular basis, and everyone seems delighted that they have apples printed on them instead of books.

Early on, the store began keeping a list of the different ways Kennebunkport was misspelled on their incoming mail. Soon the list was long enough to post in the store; then folks in the community began bringing in misspellings they had received, to add to the list; the store is now selling canvas book bags, on one side of which is the list of misspellings with the shop's logo superimposed.

A fire almost destroyed this store several years ago, but brought tremendous support and moral strength from the community. It was only the Jegloskys' second summer in business, and they had no idea till then how important the Book Port had become in people's lives. Another of the distinguishing features of the Kennebunk Book Port is its weekly ad in the local paper, *York County Coast Star*—homey, folksy, and all about books and the lore of the store. The townspeople read it as city-folk do the society columns.

Another service the Jegloskys offer: advice on starting a bookstore. At least a dozen people have come to them over the last five years looking for advice, and they've been given all kinds of suggestions and hints.

Kennebunkport is an architectural gem. Magnificent examples of Federal houses abound in the town proper, while many and varied 1890s "stick-style" shingled cottages can be found down by the ocean. The town has the expected rocky coastline, but also some very broad and long sandy beaches. Historically, Kennebunkport was a shipbuilding town, and many of its houses were built by sea captains or wealthy merchants in the early 1800s.

The Book Port couldn't be easier to find; it's right in the main square of the town, Dock Square. There's a creek behind the building where the schooners from the West Indies used to come in and tie up to unload the rum and molasses. Did the sailors buy books?

10 Dock Square, Kennebunkport, Maine 04046; Tel. 207-967-3815. Hours: Seven days a week, 10:00 A.M.–5:00 P.M.; summer hours, 10:00 A.M.–10:00 P.M.

Maryland

THE 31st STREET BOOKSTORE

This special store, co-owned by Betsy Millemann and Francine Brown, is small, but well stocked with new paperbacks (and some hardbound children's books) of fiction and nonfiction. The slant is feminist/political but there are also excellent sections on poetry, cookbooks, nature/ecology, psychology, and art. The store will special order books and also has a "half-price nook" of quality paperbacks that are slightly damaged or are on sale for other reasons.

The selection of books at the 31st Street Bookstore is done with thought and heart: the owners are less interested in the mass-market "guaranteed" best sellers than they are in carrying books that they deem, and hope their customers do also, worth reading. The key to understanding this bookstore is to know the ideas that shape its operation. The owners feel that their store is a part of the community, a typical Baltimore neighborhood, where people live and relate, as well as shop. The people in the community know the people who work in the store and vice versa, and the store owners do everything possible to cultivate the personal quality of their business, "as in the good old days." In almost poetic language, they explain: "The American city has seen some hard times, but it's undergoing a period of renaissance, restored faith, and new energy and commitment. Books are a joy. They keep people alive. They get ideas circulating which keep people growing and changing. They make change possible. A bookstore is a very special space. It should have—and keep—a very magical, turned-on quality about it. Many things happen in bookstores that,

95

perhaps, can't happen anywhere else."

425 East 31st Street, Baltimore, Maryland 21218; Tel. 301-243-3131.
Hours: Monday–Saturday, 10:00 A.M.–6:00 P.M.

THE JOHN GACH BOOKSHOP — BALTIMORE MARYLAND

"We're not quite a rare book store, but it's difficult to define what we are," says Dave Goodlaxson. He's a philosopher, a tall, youngish man with long, straight hair halfway down his back. Paradoxically, he also looks like an Ivy Leaguer. "We have odd books, as opposed to rare books. We're funky—just like the city we're in. This city has more diversified industries than any other city in the country. There's a go-go district two blocks from City Hall and the Police Department. There's also a red-light district that sailors are reported to fear next to Manila as the world's worst (or best) place to get rolled. It's the home of By-Seasoned crabs; Jack's, the world's largest pastrami deli; McCormicks spices; and Edith's Shopping Bag Thrift Store one block from the dock in historic Fall's Point, next to half-a-dozen other funky thrift shops and two Greek discos. Our bookstore was mentioned in a Playboy-type magazine in a section called 'Where the Girls Go' as a place to meet girls in Baltimore. Some deluded Johns Hopkins student sent it in."

Dave works with John Gach, who has only been in business for ten years and has done amazingly well. He's a specialist in early psychoanalytic books, but doesn't limit his activities to that field; he recently sold a first edition of Newton's *Principia* for $15,000. He operates a book-search service and keeps this "radically separate" from the store, as long as things in the store are going well. Of course, the store gets the leftovers from the book service.

A lot of haggling goes on in the store. People bring in boxes and boxes of books to sell, sometimes on their own backs. Dave tries to buy most of them. Alec, a would-be writer who also works in the store, says, "After you've spent a while going through 7,500 books, you become a perfect nihilist. I couldn't put pen to paper. I go to a lot of movies. All these books going by your eye. One hundred years from now, will your book get looked at and thrown in the basement? I wonder about it."

In total there are five employees at John Gach's: one woman is working on her Ph.D. in Classics; another, in Folklore; another is an artist who has had several shows.

Special services? There are basement sales two or three times a year, with ten to twenty thousand books at one dollar each. These are reduced to fifty cents by the end of the sale— one dollar a bag—and the sale lasts three months and may include one-hundred-year-old books! The staff know their clientele, and when they come across a book that a particular customer might be interested in, they'll call him and let him know.

"Our problem here in Baltimore is not that there aren't sufficient buyers. Nor is the problem in selling books. It's in acquiring them. This is a town with a 'Book-of-the-Month-Club' reading public. And the people who buy the more interesting books tend to hang onto them."

The people who walk into John Gach seem to be of all sorts, and, of course, there are some regular "book junkies" who buy far in excess of their own ability to read. Like many of us, they just love and need books.

3322 Greenmount Avenue, Baltimore, Maryland 21218; Tel. 301-467-4344. Hours: 10:00 A.M.–9:00 P.M., Monday–Saturday.

97

APPALACHIANA

BETHESDA
MARYLAND

Located in an attractive, open-air specialty mall in suburban Washington, D.C., Appalachiana carries thousands of volumes consisting mainly of titles on handcrafts, plus many cookbooks and books on photography. As part of a large handcraft gift shop, the book department of Appalachiana is a virtual library for those people who like to make things—almost anything—with their hands. The store carries an enormous inventory of kits and other paraphernalia for such crafts as pottery, quilts, calicos, etc., and they combine this merchandise with books on these particular subjects. Appalachiana attempts to carry every book available about each handcraft. Here are just some of the areas in which they have books: metalwork, woodworking, candle making, jewelry, decoupage, macramé, needlepoint, embroidery, crewel, beading, ceramics, collage, doll making, doll houses, weaving, and batik.

The store has hosted lectures by authors along with demonstrations, and has also conducted workshops for various crafts. Pottery is their most popular area. Owners Joan Farrell and Anne Powell and their cheerful staff are always ready and quite eager to give personal advice and information to customers on a specific craft. They will also recommend the one book that they believe is the best, considering the customer's experience and knowledge of the subject. The books they carry range from beginner's level to those for professional craftsmen.

Appalachiana accepts Master Charge and Visa cards. Although there is no catalog, per se, the store does occasionally publish a newsletter, for which there is no charge.

It's curious to note that, as a charming addition to all the other crafts one can read and learn about from Appalachiana, it is even possible to learn how to bind one's own books!

10400 Old Georgetown Road, Bethesda, Maryland 20014; Tel. 301-530-6770. Hours: Monday–Saturday, 9:30 A.M.–9:00 P.M.

PAGE ONE

COLUMBIA MARYLAND

Judy Hart, the manager of this general hardcover and paperbound bookstore, explained to us what her customers were like: "It's a mixed bag, really—women's lib as well as Barbara Cartland. *The Total Woman* and *Our Bodies, Ourselves* sold in equal numbers. We have to carry books that are intellectual opposites. We have people with a high level of education who know a lot of things about a lot of different areas."

Located in a chic, plush mall with live, healthy trees, fountains, greenhouses, and modern skylights, Page One is an excellent, service-oriented bookstore which goes out of its way to give its community what it wants and needs by way of a varied selection of books. Its customers seem to be highly interested in urban problems, sociology, black studies, and popular nonfiction, and the store carries complete sections of books in those areas.

Page One is open, airy, carpeted, and inviting, and browsing is almost a way of life there. "We are always trying to figure out what and who our customers are," says Judy Hart, "and as they change, we try to change, too."

Columbia Mall (second floor), Columbia, Maryland 21044; Tel. 301-730-8140. Hours: Monday–Saturday, 10:00 A.M.–9:30 P.M.

How many a man has dated a new era in his life from the reading of a book.

HENRY DAVID THOREAU

Massachusetts

OLD CORNER BOOK STORE

BOSTON
MASSACHUSETTS

The Old Corner Book Store is the oldest bookstore in America. The year 1828 marked its beginning as a leading influence in the literary world. In that year the store was opened by Richard Carter and Charles Hendee in an old brick building erected in 1712—and still standing—at the corner of Washington and School Streets. They planned to publish and to sell books, but soon publishing became their main interest. William D. Ticknor, an able publisher as well as bookseller, became proprietor in 1832, and under his direction the Corner Book Store became the headquarters of the geniuses of New England's golden era of letters. He introduced the works of such men as Hawthorne, De Quincey, and Charles Reade. Thackeray and Dickens were among the many great figures entertained by Ticknor and his brilliant partner, James T. Fields.

In 1859 the partners purchased a new magazine called the *Atlantic Monthly*. Fields became its editor and published the magazine in a small room at the Old Corner. Under the leadership of Ticknor and Fields, the *Atlantic* soon became America's leading literary magazine. Oliver Wendell Holmes, James Russell Lowell, Longfellow, Emerson, and Whittier were among the early contributors. The fame of the Old Corner Book Store spread throughout the English-speaking world. In a contemporary article in *Harper's Magazine*, it was said: "The Old Corner is so popular a resort that all Boston, with little exaggeration, may be said to pass through it in a day."

After Ticknor's death, the business changed hands several

100

times, but the store continued, as it has to this day, to be the haunt of Boston's literary world. The Old Corner is now a modern bookstore, but the old traditions and literary flavor have been preserved. Although no longer directly affiliated with publishing, the store frequently helps to launch new authors and publishers alike.

Visitors to the store will enjoy browsing at their leisure among a wide selection of books in both hardcover and paperback. Interesting bargains may be found in a special section.

The store's specialty is fiction, and in that category it is the best-stocked store in Boston.

In Boston, the Old Corner is a familiar landmark—one must travel outside of Boston, however, to realize the store's far-reaching influence and to appreciate the sentiment attached to it. Customers from all parts of the world—Mexico, Australia, South America, France—send for books bearing the label "The Old Corner Book Store." From the days of "all Boston" passing through its doors, the Old Corner has gone on to become a world-famous institution.

50 Bromfield St., Boston, Massachusetts 02108; Tel. 617-542-2313. Hours: Monday–Saturday, 9:00 A.M.–5:30 P.M.

THE BOOK STORE, INC   BOSTON MASSACHUSETTS

Walking through one of the most interesting and colorful neighborhoods of old Boston, down a charming cobblestoned alley, you stop at the entrance of a home built during Colonial days. There are begonias growing at the side of the house, and leading to the basement there is a white-brick wall with a bright mural of an elephant. This is the Book Store, one of Boston's most pleasant literary emporiums. Inside, the store is delight-

101

fully cluttered, like an attic, with books on the floor, stacked on tables, and anywhere there is space. And just as old attics are made to be delved into, the Book Store is ready to share its mysteries with all interested book lovers.

Located in the same area as two major publishers—Little, Brown and Houghton Mifflin—the Book Store has frequent visits by authors and editors; many of them take an affectionate, almost a proprietary interest in the store, and there are often autographing parties for authors with new books. These events are a bit more formal and elaborate than most book and author celebrations in stores: sherry or chablis, cheese and biscuits are served, and there is usually a line of people waiting to get in.

Although the Book Store sells hardbound books of all kinds and some paperbacks, the focus is on art, music and dance, architecture books, and there is also a substantial section of books on New England (many of the books the store carries in this category are out of print and virtually impossible to get anywhere else in Boston). The Book Store is also well known for its large stock of children's books. The owners feel that parents often panic at the thought of buying children's books and that if they don't receive help, they invariably choose "safe" titles. They do everything they can to assist them in making a more considered choice among some of the other books worthy of attention.

The Book Store, to some extent, is an anachronism. The look and feel of the store makes it seem out of the 1800s. The store personnel will spend an inordinate amount of time attempting to locate a book for a customer, and they maintain a large charge-account file, unusual for a small store. The shop will also make deliveries in the neighborhood, a practice that is unheard of in most bookstores anywhere in the world. These "old-fashioned" operations keep old customers but are costly and time-consuming. "It's hard to express what we give to a customer," says Carrier, "without sounding idealistic. It's not really the service we give—although we feel there's virtually nothing we won't do for our customers—but it's a sense of style which transcends a business relationship with the people who frequent our store." Apparently, this style has been warmly acceptable to the book browsers and has translated itself into success: the Book Store's business is up 100 percent over previous years.

76 Chestnut Street, Boston, Massachusetts 02108; Tel. 617-742-4531. Hours: Monday–Saturday, 10:00 A.M.–6:00 P.M.

THE BRATTLE BOOK SHOP
BOSTON MASSACHUSETTS

The Brattle Book Shop is the successor to the oldest used-book store continuously operating in the United States. And each year the Brattle is in business it adds more and more books to its stock: the store now has over 450,000 volumes spread throughout a four-story building.

Owned for three decades by George Gloss, a humorous, owlish man in his sixties, the Brattle carries just about any kind of book that anyone could possibly want. Aside from an enormous collection of fiction, the Brattle has forty-nine sections of nonfiction, one thousand titles on New England alone. Gloss draws the line on books concerning perversions. Flashers need not browse here.

It is possible at the Brattle to buy a ten-cent copy of *Love with a Harvard Accent* or a copy of *Finnegans Wake*, signed by James Joyce, for $750. But the Brattle sells a cornucopia of items other than books: presidential autographs, maps, brochures on streetcars and railroads, postcards and stereoscopic slides, old movie magazines, valentines, and old theater programs. Gloss refuses to issue a catalog, however, claiming it's adequate for him to know the whereabouts of every book himself: "It's all meticulously catalogued in my mind," he says, "and anyway, a catalogue is a waste of time. By the time it's out we will have probably sold the item."

Gloss originally fell in love with books when he was five years old and got his first library card from the East Boston Public Library; he would cart home as many books as he was allowed. He has been buying books all his life, and aside from his store, his house and garage are filled with enough volumes to stock a number of libraries. Gloss's parents owned a little store, a Dickensian-like curiosity shop which sold everything from hooks and needles to old clothing, and it was from them that he got his training as to how to operate a store. It seems that everything he did in his life, including attending Boston University, primed him for his life as a bookseller. "I'm an exceedingly rare person," he says. "I'm working at something I love."

5 West St., Boston, Massachusetts 02111; Tel. 617-542-0210. Hours: Monday–Saturday, 9:00 A.M.–5:30 P.M.

ASIAN BOOKS   CAMBRIDGE MASSACHUSETTS

In 1975, when Walter Sedgwick, a young Harvard graduate interested in Asian studies opened his bookstore near campus, he was uncertain whether there would be enough interest in what some booksellers might think was a somewhat narrow field. He wanted to specialize in those subjects in which he had personal knowledge of: Asia, the Middle East, and Africa. He soon discovered that the location for his store was ideal. There were enough scholars at Harvard and nearby schools who would become constant visitors to the store, and the Cambridge area itself had many people interested in the kinds of volumes Asian Books began to stock. In addition, seminars and colloquiums on Asian, Middle Eastern, and African studies were held frequently at Harvard, bringing experts from all over the country and the world, and a visit to Asian Books has now become *de rigeur* for those interested in finding obscure works not available anywhere else. The store has a pleasant, modern atmosphere with low, wooden benches, brick walls, exposed stained wood and plush carpeting. It is a relaxing spot to browse. Asian Books' sections began to grow, from three shelves on India, for example, to over eight today. The China and Japan sections, as well as the Middle Eastern section are especially good, but there are equally important sections on Buddhism, African art, art of other cultures, history, literature, and languages.

Asian Books issues a catalog on Middle Eastern books. It is available, free of charge, for the asking.

Kathy Grosscup, who works with Sedgwick, summed up the store's philosophy:

"We like the idea that we can be a contributor and a resource to people. We do what we can to have comprehensive coverage of a subject, but not to overstock with books of little interest. We try to remain realistic and viable."

12 Arrow Street; Cambridge, Massachusetts 02138; Tel. 617-354-0005; Hours: Monday–Saturday, 10:00 A.M.–6:00 P.M.

THE SCIENCE FANTASY BOOKSTORE   CAMBRIDGE MASSACHUSETTS

There are now over fifty bookstores in the United States and Canada that specialize in science fiction and fantasy, and this is one of the largest and certainly one of the best. Owner Spike MacPhee keeps some ten thousand books in stock: new, used, hardbound, and paperback. He also carries magazines, posters, original art work, T-shirts, and greeting cards. "Most science fiction stores carry other kinds of books, such as the occult, but we *only* carry science fiction and fantasy," says McPhee.

The store gives a 10 percent discount to any customer who pays a five-dollar-a-year membership fee; members also receive an annual catalog.

MacPhee has read every book in the store and is a gold mine of information on science fiction. He attends many SF conventions and is used as a source of knowledge by the media and even by scientists from M.I.T. "We attempt to provide an environment where we can answer people's questions, serve them in any way we can, and provide as much service as we can while keeping the store as well stocked as any on the continent." Or the planet?

18 Eliot Street, Cambridge, Massachusetts 02138; Tel. 617-547-5917. Hours: Tuesday–Saturday, 11:00 A.M.–6:30 P.M.; Thursday till 8:00 P.M.

SCHOENHOF'S   CAMBRIDGE
MASSACHUSETTS

Perhaps you're interested in the origin of a word from the Old Norse. Or you want to read Freud in the original German. Or your company is sending you abroad for a year and you must learn Welsh . . . or Persian . . . or Armenian . . . or any one of a hundred different languages. The place to go is Schoenhof's, the oldest (1856), largest, and best foreign-language bookstore in the world.

Schoenhof's carries some 25,000 to 30,000 books in various languages, and it is possible to find dictionaries, grammar books, literature, and other works in virtually any of the major—or minor—languages of the world. The store's heaviest

106

concentration is in books concerning French, Spanish, German, Italian, Russian, Polish, Portuguese, Greek, Latin, Ukrainian, Modern Greek, and Yiddish.

Books on linguistics, etymology, and the history of language are also carried, a collection built over the years by John Furattini, the owner and manager. "To find what we have here," he says, "you would have to go to 2,000 to 3,000 bookstores across the globe. We feel the store is a service to the scholarly community." Schoenhof's also carries children's books in Danish, Swedish, Italian, and Spanish—to serve the small colonies of foreign families in the area.

Schoenhof's is so well known by people who are interested—or become so—in the study of languages that they do no advertising, make no mailings. The store's publicity is entirely word of mouth, and scholars come back thirty years after leaving Harvard to buy books there. The store has been catering to the famous for years: Octavio Paz, Marc Chagall, Noam Chomsky have all dealt there. On the wall is a framed check for $49.35 from none other than William James. Poet Lawrence Ferlinghetti, himself the owner of a bookstore, once wrote a poem that referred to the store:

> "But when guns are roaring
> The Muses have no right to be silent!"
> says a book on Russian poets
> I pick up free at Schoenhof's.

Furattini laughingly says that when he was in California he wanted to go to Ferlinghetti's City Lights Books and demand that he pay for that book but decided to forget it at the last moment.

Furattini is himself a book lover: "A bookman has to be a book lover," he says, "especially in a small store. Dealing with books is not only my business, it's my pleasure."

1280 Massachusetts Avenue, Cambridge, Massachusetts 02138; Tel. 617-547-8855, 56, 57. Hours: Monday–Friday, 9:00 A.M.–6:00 P.M.

HARVARD COOP

When the Harvard Coop celebrates its 100th anniversary in 1982, it will undoubtedly be a festive occasion to remember: the store has been a successful operation almost from the first day it opened its doors and still continues to progress from year to year. In 1970, it gave its cooperative members a 2 percent rebate at the end of the year. In 1977 it gave them a whopping 8 percent. Eighty thousand members belong.

One of the reasons the Harvard Coop is such a good store is its superior management—all department heads go through an executive training program—and the development of its personnel on all levels is one of the store's primary concerns. All of this translates into concern for its customers: Harvard and M.I.T. students and faculty, residents of Cambridge and Boston—all among the best-educated people in the country.

The store carries some sixty thousand titles of new hardbound and paperback books. On the first floor, where the stock consists mainly of hardbacks, the shelves are dark wood, there is carpeting, and the tables, walls, and displays of books are all attractively and efficiently arranged. Although the Coop is most definitely a general bookstore, its sections and specializations are virtually small stores within themselves. The children's section is one of the best in the country, as is the travel section. The Coop carries some 700–800 cookbooks alone—most well-stocked stores rarely carry over 100.

The second floor has some 18,000 to 20,000 paperbacks, a very large collection of classical records (which are discounted by 25 percent to 35 percent), educational games, posters, and prints. There is also a framing shop.

The third floor consists of remainder books and reference volumes and related texts. On any given day this floor is jammed with professionals looking for books in their field and students picking up copies of the texts needed in their courses.

Each floor has a customer service desk, and each sales clerk is responsible not only for selling books, but also for the stock, so that each keeps apprised of what is needed and where.

When the Harvard Coop has an autograph party, it becomes almost a news event, as it was when Muhammed Ali gave a press conference there or when Alistair Cooke drew more than a thousand people to the store.

Dan de Lellis, the director of the bookstore, went to Boston University, ostensibly majoring in English literature, "but really majoring in bookstores," during his four-year apprenticeship there. He is the one who so heavily promotes the emphasis on good relations with employees and customers: "People, all the people, are the most important part of the store."

Harvard Square, 1400 Mass. Avenue, Cambridge, Massachusetts 02138; Tel. 617-492-1000. Hours: Monday–Saturday, 9:20 A.M.–5:45 P.M.; Thursdays, till 8:30 P.M.

Camerado, this is no book.
Who touches this, touches a man.

WALT WHITMAN

109

Harvard Book Store, Cambridge, Massachusetts

HARVARD BOOK STORES

CAMBRIDGE MASSACHUSETTS

Jess Joseph, the principal buyer and merchandise manager for the Harvard Book Stores, knows a great deal about books and book trends: "Students used to do a tremendous amount of reading outside of their courses, but now they're more worried about jobs and they've switched from the so-called soft majors to the hard—business, economics, medicine. They're concerned about grades; less likely to explore outside required course books. They've become less adventurous in their reading habits. Interestingly, the post-modernist writers, such as Heller and Pynchon, have gained at the expense of Joyce and Faulkner. Also the new generation of readers seem to be interested in Victorian novels more than ever before—George Eliot, Charlotte Brontë, Balzac, and others."

This ability to analyze and keep abreast of the reading interests of its customers makes Harvard Book Stores one of the better bookstores in New England. Actually an amalgam of three stores in Cambridge, two next door to each other and one around the corner, and two stores in Boston, Harvard Book Stores can be considered a mini-chain.

There are three stores in Cambridge instead of one simply because space is at a premium and difficult to secure; otherwise, the stock would be housed under a single roof.

The corner store carries new hardcover and paperback books; the shop next store is stocked with sale books, damaged books, and remainders, with a balcony of secondhand textbooks at 25 percent discount and a basement of used paperbacks at 50 percent off the retail price; around the corner, in the *Harvard Crimson* building, is an enormous stock of lawbooks, casebooks, textbooks, and study guides. The store on Commonwealth Avenue in Boston, across from Boston University, although not the official bookstore of the university, is

111

said to give the best student service of any store in the area—
and carries books for the university's philosophy, classics, English, social studies, and foreign language departments, together with new and remaindered hardcover titles and new and used lawbooks. The store on Newbury Street is the official store of the New England School of Law and, in addition to lawbooks, carries other hardcovers, paperbacks, and remainders. In total, all the stores have upwards of 125,000 books in stock.

The store issues a catalog, does free gift-wrapping, will special order any book, and encourages mail orders.

The clerks in all the stores seem to be on the same wavelength as the customers. They are well read and well educated and are inveterate book buyers themselves. There is a large section in the stockroom of books placed on reserve for future purchase by people who work in the store.

1256 Massachusetts Avenue (main store), Cambridge, Massachusetts 02138; Tel. 617-661-1515. Hours: Monday–Saturday, 9:30 A.M.– 10:00 P.M.; Sunday, 12:00 Noon–8:00 P.M.

GROLIER BOOK SHOP   CAMBRIDGE MASSACHUSETTS

The Grolier Book Shop is one of the finest poetry bookshops in the country, with a minor specialization in women's and gay literature.

Founded over fifty years ago, the Grolier was started under the inspiration of Conrad Aiken, who lived upstairs from Gordon Cairnie, who was the original owner. Aiken wrote in *Ushanti*: "And, now and again, too, the Good Grolier, the beneficent spider, would ascend from his cobweb of a bookshop, below stairs, bringing the loan of an armful of books and a ham sandwich, in exchange for a snort of gin."

In addition to Aiken, the Grolier has served over the years as the literary gathering place of Richard Eberhard, Thornton Wilder, Allen Ginsberg, Robert Lowell, Marianne Moore, Gary Snyder, and E. E. Cummings. An old brown leather couch, with rusty springs and cigarette holes, sunk down in the center with unopened mail and publishers' catalogs, has served for years as the rostrum of the poets, who drank coffee, held forth, and "talked down to the women," according to Louisa.

There is a special charm to the Grolier: old photographs on the wall stretching to the highest corner of the twenty-foot ceilings; hanging plants; floorboards that creak; extra folding chairs in the corner.

Books are arranged alphabetically on the shelves and tables: *Parnassus, 13th Moon, American Poetry Review*; a biography of Mabel Dodge Luhan; the *Whole Word Catalogue; Writers' Resources*; one bookcase of prose; *City Lights Anthology*; Blaise Cendrars' *Complete Postcards from the Americas* and postcard poetry by a new poet; *Sparrow,* published by Black Sparrow Press, 1973–77; *Painted Fans of Japan, Fifteen Noh Drama Masterpieces*—each book a find.

Grolier no longer has readings at the store because it's too small for the crowds the poetry events attract. The store does cosponsor a poetry award with Blacksmith House, and the winner goes on to do a reading and receives a small fee.

Grolier will appraise books, order books for a customer, search for and trace books. The store also posts announcements concerning poetry contests and serves as the information center for poetry events in the Boston area. One of the most interesting things about the Grolier, according to Louisa, is the strange and wonderful people who inhabit her store, who become her friends and later go on to publish their work. "I like that a lot," she says, smiling.

6 Plympton Street, Cambridge, Massachusetts 02138; Tel. 617-547-4648. Hours: Monday, 11:30 A.M.–3:30 P.M., 4:00 P.M.–6:00 P.M.;

THE MARKET BOOKSHOP

FALMOUTH MASSACHUSETTS

Located on the opposite end of Cape Cod from Province-town, the town of Falmouth is an old New England village that draws thousands of tourists in the summertime, but has a steady, year-round group of residents. Both the tourists and the regulars use the Market Bookshop as their principal source of literary nourishment. On a pleasant street with plenty of parking, Market Bookshop has a charming interior: a fireplace that is always going on cold and damp days, with a table and chairs in front of it; plenty of other places to sit; a children's corner; an art gallery in the barn at the back of the store. The building is almost one hundred years old and for almost all of that time was *the* butcher shop for the town, catering to the summer trade, the wealthy estate owners nearby, and the local townspeople. Now, the old butcher block is the library table, and the store's office is the former cold-storage room. Browsing is officially encouraged.

Although the store has a substantial section of books on New England, Cape Cod, marine science, and nature, it really is a general bookstore with over fifty thousand new titles in stock at any one time.

The owners, William and Caroline Banks, conduct approximately four autograph parties each year. They will special order a book for a customer, and they have a mailing list. Anyone can be placed on the list simply by asking. "It's interesting to note the trends, the fads and fashions of people," says Bill Banks, "and how they wax and wane. One year you sell a significant number of bicycle books. This year everyone is

114

The Market Bookshop, Falmouth, Massachusetts

interested in solar energy and simple things like wood heat. We're excited by the idea that every day we're putting books in the hands of people who love them."

15 Depot Avenue, Falmouth, Massachusetts 02540; Tel. 617-548-5636. Hours: Monday–Saturday, 9:00 A.M.–5:30 P.M.; Wednesday, 9:00 A.M.–11:00 P.M.; summer hours, Monday–Saturday, 9:00 A.M.–9:00 P.M.; Sunday, 10:00 A.M.–4:00 P.M.

'Tis the good reader that makes the good book.
RALPH WALDO EMERSON

The Birmingham Bookstore, Birmingham, Michigan

Michigan

THE BIRMINGHAM BOOKSTORE

Joyce Carol Oates is a frequent visitor to the Birmingham Bookstore. As she browses through the aisles, she probably goes unnoticed by the many people from the automobile industry—Chrysler and General Motors—who also frequent this fine general bookstore. Opened in 1975 by Betti and Sol Kurtzman, the Birmingham Bookstore carries close to twenty thousand titles and is greatly varied in subject matter. The store's most ambitious section consists of books about Michigan and the Great Lakes, but it also has one of the best foreign-language sections in the state, with books in French, German, Italian, Spanish, and Latin. The store also carries, maps, greeting cards, and bookends.

Soon after it opened, the Birmingham started a series of Sunday seminars which have proved to be a popular sellout. Such topics as children's literature, women and the middle years, and sex education have been discussed by experts in the field. Mrs. Kurtzman elaborated on how she and her husband feel about their store: "We want to serve our customers and the best way to do this is to know them. We try to. We also want to serve our community, and we keep in touch and participate in civic activities. This is the role of a good bookstore."

263 Pierce St., Birmingham, Michigan 48011; Tel. 313-642-4404. Hours: Monday, Tuesday, Wednesday, and Saturday, 10:00 A.M – 5:30 P.M.; Thursday and Friday, 10:00 A.M.–9:00 P.M.

Minnesota

THE BOOK POST

**DULUTH
MINNESOTA**

Barbara Landfield, the owner of the Book Post, describes her store as a one-horse operation, "and I'm the horse," she says humorously. She does, in fact, operate the store herself, with help from her son, since the untimely death, in 1977, of her husband, but she has remained undaunted, although sometimes overwhelmed, by the work it takes to run what some people consider one of the best bookstores in the entire state. Even visitors from the comparatively sophisticated city of Minneapolis often say of the Book Post, "I wish we had a store like this down there."

Located in what used to be a post office, on a residential street, the building is old, charming, and well built. The interior of the store looks more like a living room or someone's personal library than a commercial establishment—Barbara has decorated it with lamps and pictures and furniture of her own. As one new woman customer recently said, "This is the first bookstore I've ever felt at home in."

The store is small, but filled with a treasure of backlist classics. There are approximately ten thousand titles in stock, but they are all *different* new paperback and hardbound fiction and nonfiction books. Locally, the Book Post has the best collection of philosophy, poetry, juvenile books, and classical literature, and it is fast building an entire Mark Twain section. The store has a sale table with constant bargains and also sells greeting cards, note paper, posters, art prints, and some adult games like chess and backgammon. Author autograph parties are held occasionally and Barbara often lectures about the book business; sometimes book reviews appear under her name in local club publications. The Book Post will mail books anywhere and does special gift-wrapping. A newsletter/catalog, "The Book-Let," is published annually, and anyone can be placed on the mailing list simply by writing to the store. The poetry section is also uncommonly good—poet Robert Bly, a visitor to the store, helped stock the section by making suggestions.

The Book Post reflects the philosophy of its owner: it is a store that is somewhat like a library and has a small selection of just about any kind of book. Barbara believes that a bookseller should be avant-garde, or at least a little ahead of her customers, so that when they become interested in something, she will already have a book on that subject in stock. "The bookseller should, ideally, be a community educator," she avers, "and one who is not afraid to take chances on the books that he sells." The Book Post's slogan, emblazoned on its letterhead, is "Uncommon Books and Unusual Things."

2311 Woodland Avenue, Duluth, Minnesota 55803; Tel. 218-724-6056. Hours: Monday–Saturday, 10:00 A.M.–5:30 P.M.; Sunday, 2:00 P.M.–5:00 P.M.

GNOSTICA BOOKSTORE   MINNEAPOLIS MINNESOTA

Take a former large, drafty mortuary, paint it purple, and you've got the perfect setting for an occult bookstore. Gnostica, the retail arm of Llewellyn Publications, which is a large publisher and wholesaler of occult books, is run by Carl Weschke, himself a warlock. Llewellyn was earning $40,000 a year when Weschke bought it in 1960. Today he has run this up to $850,000 a year and has become an important publisher and seller of occult books.

Here, books are arranged by subject matter, mixing fiction

120

with nonfiction, and you'll find serious books on any given subject mixed in with lighter works.

People who believe seriously in astrology will always consult the stars via the book of numbers and will make sure that the papers of incorporation are stamped at precisely the time and day that the stars deem most propitious for the success of any venture. Accordingly, after much astrological consultation, Gnostica was opened precisely at 8:02 A.M. on January 15, 1970.

Many occult bookshops have found it difficult to keep in business, but Gnostica is doing well. The patrons cross all age barriers and come from all walks of life. And they buy more than books, for the store also stocks tarot cards, thuribles, incense, and scented oils. In the glass showcases customers can find amulets and scarabs, and these are not just novelties, for the people who come to Gnostica take a serious interest in occult objects.

Because Weschke also wholesales books, his publication, *Aquarian Age Prevue*, focuses on new books in the occult and usually carries many of his books. Weschke points out that there is an occult renaissance in progress and that, prior to this development, serious books on astrology and the occult were too sophisticated for the average bookstore. Sales were mainly by direct mail and to a limited number of outlets, such as Weiser's in New York and Gilbert's in Los Angeles. But times have changed and people, growing more involved, are interested in books with more depth than Linda Goodman's *Sun Signs*.

Plans are now under way to open a second store in St. Paul, and this consolidation will leave room for Weschke to conduct classes in the Minneapolis shop. "Gnostica will become a learning center," Weschke says, and hopes.

Gnostica sponsors an Autumnal Festival, a recent one spanning some three weeks. The focus is on astrology, parapsychology, and witchcraft. In addition to publicizing Llewellyn authors, the festival encourages people to come together and exchange ideas and knowledge of the occult.

Weschke offers daily astrological readings to a Twin Cities audience via the radio and is often seen on local television, discussing the occult. This media exposure invariably brings new people into Gnostica seeking the world views of Zarathustra or the Jungian interpretation of dreams.

213 E. 4th St., St. Paul, Minnesota 55101; Tel. 612-291-1970. P.O. Box 3383, St. Paul Minnesota 55165. Hours: Monday–Saturday, 10:00 A.M.–5:30 P.M.

SAVRAN'S PAPERBACK SHOP   MINNEAPOLIS MINNESOTA

"Books deserve more than a few months' shelf-life," says owner William Savran, "and we try to keep a good selection of books, both old and new, for as long as possible."

Savran's Paperback Shop (which sells hardcovers, too) is a store in the tradition of City Lights Bookstore in San Francisco or Barbara's Bookstore in Chicago: an enormous selection of poetry and small press literature; a heavy emphasis on theatre, film, and the humanities; and a store filled with books (about twenty-five thousand) of a general nature. It's located near the University of Minnesota in an older area with other interesting shops nearby, and the neighborhood is a good one to stroll in and window-shop.

Savran's encourages browsers and conducts readings and other events from time to time. Gary Snyder, Diane Wakoski, Robert Bly, and Dianne di Prima are just some of the poets who have visited the store over the years. "The store reflects the interests of our employees," says Savran. "Fortunately, they have the same interests as our customers."

301 Cedar Avenue, Minneapolis, Minnesota 55454; Tel. 612-333-0098. Hours: Monday–Friday, 10:00 A.M.–9:00 P.M.; Saturday, 10:00 A.M.–5:30 P.M.

HUNGRY MIND
BOOKSTORE

ST. PAUL
MINNESOTA

Angela Davis buys books there. Kate Millett browses on occasion. Local poets of regional fame often come in to study the extensive poetry section and pick up a copy of the latest alternative magazine or newspaper. Located near Macalester College, in a small section of specialty shops known as Mac Market, the Hungry Mind is a large bookstore that tries to provide good service, low prices, and a wide selection of titles. It succeeds in all categories.

The store stocks mostly new books, paperbound and hardcover, fiction and nonfiction, but it also carries used textbooks as a service to the students of the two colleges nearby. The community around the store is one of professionals, students, and "aging hippies," and the store specializes in small press and poetry books, in which its customers show great interest. The sections of juvenile literature and books on psychology are also substantial.

There are usually things happening at the Hungry Mind: autograph parties, tastings for cookbooks, and poetry readings. The store is informal, and people have been known to lie down on the sofa at the back of the store, take a nap, and then resume browsing. No one minds.

R. David Unowsky, the owner of the Hungry Mind, makes sure that there is a pleasant atmosphere for browsers. "We want to provide a broad selection of books representing the needs and wants of our community while maintaining a standard of literary quality and to do this as cheaply and as efficiently as possible. We also want people to have a nice time here."

1648 Grand Avenue, St. Paul, Minnesota 55105; Tel. 612-699-0587. Hours: Monday, Tuesday, Thursday, and Friday, 9:00 A.M.–8:00 P.M.; Wednesday, 9:00 A.M.–6:00 P.M.; Saturday, 10:00 A.M.–6:00 P.M.

123

Nebraska

NEBRASKA BOOKSTORE   **LINCOLN**
                                          NEBRASKA

The day Dick Cavett came into the Nebraska Bookstore—
the prodigy returning to his old home state—everyone in the
store was aflutter. Dick signed autographs, traded cynical
quips with some of his old schoolmates, and checked on how his
autobiography was selling. It was an interesting afternoon for
everyone.

Located on the southwest edge of the University of Nebraska
campus, the Nebraska Bookstore is one of the best-stocked
literary establishments in the entire state: some seventy
thousand books, paperbound and hardback, fiction and nonfiction, new, used, and rare, all spread out in a composite of nine
buildings.

In addition to the quantity and quality of stock, Nebraska
Bookstore also conducts a varied program of events, literary
and otherwise: puppet shows, autographings, a children's
hour, chess demonstrations, and other lectures and readings.
Around Christmas time, there is always punch and cookies.

Cards, posters, maps, art supplies, and an entire line of "Big
Red" items are also carried by the store and dispensed with
knowledge and efficiency by the fifty full-time employees. The
store accepts Visa credit cards and Master Charge.

Owner George Lincoln is emphatic in requiring that the
store clerks follow his personal philosophy of bookselling: "I
would rather talk a person out of the 'wrong' book than let him
buy it. If I can help someone find what he needs (not just what
he asks for) and at a reasonable price, I can build repeat
business. This brand of service is good for us and good for our
customers."

1135 R Street, Lincoln, Nebraska 68508; Tel. 402-432-0111. Hours: Monday–Saturday, 8:00 A.M.–5:00 P.M.

My encounters with books I regard very much as my encounters with other phenomena of life or thought. All encounters are configurate, not isolate. In this sense, and in this sense only, books are as much a part of my life as trees, stars or dung.

HENRY MILLER

New Hampshire

DARTMOUTH BOOKSTORE

HANOVER
NEW HAMPSHIRE

Because the campus of beautiful Dartmouth College is virtually at the front door of the Dartmouth Bookstore, it's only natural that many young college students stop in and buy their books there. Most of the students are not affluent, and every cent they spend is like torture for them. A typical student will scream about the high cost of books, after tallying up some sixty dollars' worth of them, and then when the screaming stops, he'll plunk down another ten dollars or so for records. The store prospers.

This shop was founded in 1872 by Nelson McLary and sold to Edward Payson Storrs in 1883. It is now owned by Mr. Storrs's granddaughter, employs twenty-four people, and boasts a stock of thirty-five to forty thousand books, all new, both hardbound and paperback, fiction and nonfiction. The specialty here, if it can be called that, is a 1600-square-foot children's department, but because the shop is located on a main street, the stock is classified as general, although a large part of the volume is in textbooks for the college trade. The store will search for out-of-print books and will special order books that are not presently in stock.

The staff here is promotion-conscious, and they have occasional autograph parties and conduct an annual Halloween party for the kids. They also do a radio show, called "Where the Sidewalk Ends," to promote children's books and another, called "Between the Pages," to promote books to adults. They mail all over the world, and you can get on the mailing list by sending in your name and address. Browsers here are some-

126

times notables. You might look up from a book you are examining to find Charles Bronson or J. D. Salinger across the aisle. And, in addition to books, you'll find records, school supplies, posters, art supplies, puzzles, toys, and calculators, and now, since the calculator supplier sells digital watches, a complete line of those as well.

The shop is easy to locate, I-89 and I-91 connect across the Connecticut River in White River Junction, and you take I-91 North to Hanover. You'll find the shop on Main Street. Right around the corner is Hopkins Center, rural New England's cultural center. The philosophy here is to fit as many books as possible into the store, surround them with a knowledgeable staff and friendly atmosphere, allow leisurely customer browsing with good directional signs, and, finally, to get any book that can be found for a customer. The store seems to succeed in all attempts.

33 South Main Street, Hanover, New Hampshire 03755; Tel. 603-643-3616. Hours: Monday–Saturday, 8:30 A.M.–5:00 P.M.

Books must be read as deliberately
and reservedly as they are written.
                              HENRY DAVID THOREAU

New Mexico

CABLE'S BOOK STORE

SANTA FE
NEW MEXICO

Located on one of Santa Fe's most active and attractive plazas, Cable's is undoubtedly one of the most sophisticated bookstores in the entire Southwest. It is also one of the most successful, judging by the number of customers and browsers who come into the shop each day. In addition to hardbound and paperback books (and there is a great stock of books in just about every subject), Cable's carries a full selection of cards and maps, an entire department of elegant posters, and a large selection of books about both the past and the contemporary Southwest. It is also possible to purchase here a libretto of any of the operas performed at the Santa Fe Opera House. In addition, Cable's is known for its good selection of modern educational materials for students of all ages. The store often conducts sales of these materials, and as a result, it has become a favorite among teachers in the Santa Fe area. Cable's services mail-order requests, and if a book is out of stock or the store doesn't carry it, the staff will secure it for the customer if it is in print. The shop accepts all major credit cards.

What is the secret of Cable's success, and how does it manage to have just about any book that is requested? Arthur G. Cable, the store's owner, put it succinctly: "We love books and we work like hell to get the best books into the store for our customers!"

72 East San Franscico, "On the Plaza," Santa Fe, New Mexico 87501; Tel. 505-982-9542. Hours: Monday–Saturday, 9:30 A.M.–5:00 P.M.

New York

SECOND STORY

CHAPPAQUA
NEW YORK

"We don't have much depth, but we have the broadest spread possible. Booksellers are astounded at the number of titles. We cover the waterfront," so says Joan Ripley, the owner of Second Story, in New York's affluent Westchester County.

The store is inviting because there are so many titles packed in: it's interesting, but somehow not cluttered, with toys and knickknacks on one wall, cards and children's books in the back, a bargain table out front and also outside. The shop is located in a little colonial house on a street that curves up the hill, so that you enter directly into the second story, where the store is located.

Joan has five children and a degree in chemistry, and a few years ago, when she decided to go back to work, she opened the bookstore after serving an apprenticeship at Anderson's in nearby Larchmont. "Most people have a foolish idea of what bookselling is all about," she says. "They think that you sit around reading, discussing O'Neill and Camus and, if you're a man, you philosophically puff away at a pipe. But the reality is that bookselling is a retail business and you must know your stock, your customer, and yourself. It's exciting."

The store carries a general stock of hardbound and paperback books and specializes in education and books on learning disabilities, which are obviously not big sellers, but are provided as a service to the community.

Second Story's brightly colored paper bags, imprinted with a menagerie of animals, have become the store's trademark. People often come in, saying, "I didn't really want a book, but I sure wanted a bag." Someone was even seen on a beach in Egypt with the bag he had kept.

The store has outdoor sales in the patio and conducts about six autograph parties a year, at which champagne punch is served. The shop also has photo exhibits and book fairs, and the staff works closely with the local book clubs.

Children seem to love the store. One night Joan had locked the store and was on her way out through the patio when she heard a knocking coming from inside the store. It was a small child who had become so absorbed in reading that he had gotten locked in among the books.

95 King St., Chappaqua, New York 10514; Tel. 914-238-4463. Hours: Monday–Saturday, 9:30 A.M.–5:30 P.M.

ANDERSON'S   LARCHMONT
BOOK SHOP   NEW YORK

Walter Kerr, drama critic of the *New York Times*, is a frequent and ardent browser. Bennett Cerf, the late publisher of Random House, often stopped by. Some fifty local authors are numbered among the regular customers.

Wanting to start a small bookstore after the Second World War, Charles B. Anderson opened "hardly more than a cubicle," as he described it, in 1946, to serve the town of Larchmont in Westchester County, north of New York City. As Mr. Anderson became more sophisticated in the ways of bookselling—he eventually was elected and served as the president of the American Booksellers Association—and learned not only what his customers wanted, but how he could get books from publishers and distributors in the fastest and most economical way, the store grew and grew and grew and is now the principal bookshop in the area, selling more trade books than any other bookstore in Westchester County, an affluent, book-buying community.

Now owned by William R. Buschal, Anderson's shelves are stocked with over eighty thousand books—twenty-five thousand different titles at any given time—and has large sections of books on sailing and boating, gardening, crafts, and cooking, as well as one of the most complete juvenile sections in the New York area. The store carries both hardbound and paperback books, both fiction and nonfiction, as well as greeting cards, social stationery, jigsaw puzzles, and candles. It has become an efficient, service-oriented bookstore: Anderson's will order any book in print and ship it anywhere, and its clerks are so adept at gift-wrapping that people drive from miles around to take advantage of their artistry, especially at Christmas time. The store accepts Visa and Master Charge credit cards. Mail-order buyers—and Anderson's has them all over the world—can receive their catalogs free of charge by simply writing to the store.

Anderson's role in the community goes beyond the all-important job of supplying books to readers. The store's personnel are involved in many Westchester activities, and the shop frequently cosponsors readings and book-and-author luncheons as fund-raising events for various civic groups.

Publishers throughout the United States use Anderson's as a "test" store. Advance copies of books are put on sale there to determine how much promotion a certain title will need in the rest of the country, according to the sales of the book at Anderson's. The Anderson "sales barometer" has become famous in other quarters as well: for twenty-five years, the store has been reporting its sales figures on a weekly basis to the *New York Times*, and the number of books sold at Anderson's combined with the figures from other key stores make up the famous best-seller list of the *Times*, the most influential such list in the country.

Anderson's is perhaps the only bookstore in America to have been immortalized by a Pulitzer-Prize–winning poet. Here is

131

Phyllis McGinley's poem about the store:

A Toast

Here's three loud cheers and one cheer more
For Mr. Anderson's brand-new store
Where aisle and counter and stack and shelf
Look fresh and gracious as Spring itself.

Here's to a shop serenely housing
Books for borrowing, buying, browsing;
Ripe to rival in dozens of ways
Scribner's, Brentano's or Doubleday's.

Yet happily spiced for all to savor
With local tang and a Village flavor
That marks it *Anderson's*, his alone:
Westchester's pride but Larchmont's own.

96–98 Chatsworth Avenue, Larchmont, New York 10538; Tel. 914-834-6900. Hours: Monday–Saturday, 9:00 A.M.–6:00 P.M.

CHINA BOOKS   NEW YORK NEW YORK

On Manhattan's lower Fifth Avenue—the section below Twenty-third Street—there is an area that is becoming known as "booksellers' row," consisting of a number of large, clean, brightly lit stores that specialize in new books in foreign languages or from foreign publishers. Nearby is the gigantic Barnes & Noble sales annex, noted elsewhere as the largest bookstore in the world.

One of the most distinguished shops in the neighborhood is China Books. Although not an agency of the People's Republic of China (the store is privately owned by Henry Noyes, who was born in Canton, China, lived there until he was eight years old, and still visits from time to time), it is in this country the principal distributor, importer, and seller of books, periodicals, and pamphlets from and about China. There are actually three stores—the other two are in San Francisco and Chicago—which not only serve retail customers but supply some two thousand other bookstores and many bookbuyers who come into the stores with material from China. The store fills orders from such governmental agencies as the U.S. State Department and the Library of Congress.

Thousands of books, pamphlets, records, pins, prints, cards, and other merchandise, all pertaining to China or to the social and political aspects of other countries (especially in the Third World but also including the U.S.) can be bought at China Books. The most popular work is the well-known "little red book," *Quotations from Chairman Mao Tse-tung*, available in various editions and prices (for as little as forty-five cents) and in thirty-six languages, including Esperanto. There are also other major works of Mao, including a five-volume set of his selected writings, in addition to many pamphlets that outline his political theories and positions.

Although some of the books carried by China Books are in Chinese, and a few are in bilingual editions, most of the publications are in English. There are books and pamphlets on Chinese life and society, art, literature and poetry, political theories, Marxist-Leninist classics, acupuncture, and many other subjects, including a complete section of fairy tales and other children's books by Chinese authors. Almost every book that is carried by China Books is inexpensive, with the exception of some of the books published by U.S. publishers about China.

The store also sells exquisite note cards made of wheatstraw and a complete line of delicate papercuts, an ancient Chinese art still very popular in China today. Subscriptions for over 50 periodicals from or about China can be placed with China Books. For those who might be planning a trip to China or who

133

want to become more immersed in its culture, China Books carries a full line of instructional tapes, records, and books for the study of modern Chinese.

A current catalog which lists most of the books and products carried by the store can be secured, free of charge, by writing to China Books. There are over 40,000 people on the mailing list.

The store's manager explains the store's philosophy: "We want to bring China to the people of the United States, and we want to do this in as friendly and open a manner as possible. Most of our customers think we have a wonderful store. We try to serve the people."

125 Fifth Avenue, New York, New York 10003; Tel. 212-677-2650. Hours: Monday–Thursday and Saturday, 10:00 A.M.–6:00 P.M.; Friday, 10:00 A.M.–7:00 P.M.

MURDER INK.® 　　　　　　　　 NEW YORK
　　　　　　　　　　　　　　　 NEW YORK

It is the annual anniversary of the St. Valentine's Day Massacre and a group of people not so solemnly mark the event by meeting every year in a New York garage (the original massacre took place in a garage on Clark Street in Chicago), where they sip Bloody Marys and munch on Italian hero sandwiches while watching crime films projected on the back wall. Sound macabre? To some, the practice may seem a little bit too haunted, but to this group of crime and mystery lovers, it is an opportunity to meet and discuss their favorite topics: death, murder, and sleuthing. The event is sponsored every year by Murder Ink., the first mystery-only bookstore in the world. Owned by Carol Brener, Murder Ink. is a small—but greatly stocked—store located on Manhattan's Upper West Side, and there are some eight thousand books to choose from, consisting

134

of mysteries, detective fiction, classic horror stories, romantic adventures, tales of espionage, and reference books about mystery books and mystery writers.

Many of Murder Ink.'s customers are psychiatrists, "perhaps because they're interested in motives," says Ms. Brener. But basically, the browsers and buyers are people who just love a good murder mystery and are avid, insatiable fans of the genre. One couple from Delaware comes to New York regularly "to have dinner at Mama Leone's and visit Murder Ink." The store is arranged by category and taste: private eye, Sherlock Holmes, adventure, spy, etc. Here it's possible to find such works as *The Annotated Dracula*, the *Catalogue of Crime*, a biography of Raymond Chandler, dozens of Nero Wolfe mysteries, many of the works of Ross Macdonald.

Ms. Brener's special recommendations for excellent mysteries: *Smallbone Deceased*, by Michael Gilbert, which she says is "wonderful, witty, beautifully written"; *The First Deadly Sin*, by Lawrence Sanders, "the *War and Peace* of mysteries"; and *Tears of Autumn*, by Charles McCarry, a spy thriller about the Kennedy assassination.

Murder Ink. services mail-order requests, will special order in-print books, gives research assistance, does searching for out-of-print books, issues gift certificates, and conducts many events (in addition to the St. Valentine's Day Massacre party), which include weekend trips, "The Dead of Winter," consisting of lectures, trips to haunted spots, and general sleuthiana. Names can be added to the mailing list upon request.

The founder, Dilys Winn, has compiled a volume of essays by murder and mystery experts. The title? *Murder Ink.: The Mystery Reader's Companion*, dedicated to Carol Brener.

271 West 87th St., New York, New York 10024; Tel. 212-362-8905. Hours: Tuesday, Wednesday, Friday, 2:00 P.M.–8:00 P.M.; Thursday, 2:00 P.M.–10:00 P.M.; Saturday, 1:00 P.M.–7:00 P.M.

It is quite an easy task—and it's certainly a pleasant one—to spend the better part of a day browsing in the Strand. It is not only one of the largest bookstores in the world but one of the most unusual. With well over two million titles, the Strand is a book addict's paradise: every available inch of the store is crammed with books, books, and more books—eight miles of shelves in total. There is constant expansion taking place. The store is labrynthal, and one can wile away hours—even days— roaming, Valjean-like, through the book-laden basement rooms. These stretch under the sidewalks of Broadway, making the Strand—or at least part of it—the only subterranean bookstore in the United States. Burt Britton, former manager, who ruled over the basement with knowledge, vivacity, and good book talk, now has his own bookstore, but his influence can still be felt.

Used books make up the greatest percentage of the Strand's stock, and for fifty years, libraries and independent buyers from all over the world have used the store constantly to fill and replenish their own collections. Here it is possible to find an obscure novel by Samson Raphaelson, out of print for decades; an esoteric chemistry text that was used in the Depression; Forbes's *History of Chess* published in the eighteen hundreds; poetry collections from the jazz age, the beatnik era, and the hippie generation. The Strand's specialties are in used books such as art, Americana, literature, history, fiction, social sciences, and economics, although there are enormous sections in drama, journalism, reference, travel, business, and dozens of other categories.

Aside from the avalanche of used books—for which it is well known—the Strand also sells new books, remainders, sale books, and paperbacks. But it is by way of its review books that it has become even more famous over the years.

Several decades ago, literary critic Clifton Fadiman came into the Strand with several boxes of books sent him by publishers wanting him to write reviews. Naturally, due to space limitations, a critic can only review a small number of books although he usually received hundreds of others for possible inclusion in his columns. Fadiman had no space in his apartment for or any interest in keeping many of the books he received. Hence, the birth of the Strand's sale of review books.

After Fadiman began to sell these mint-condition new books, many of them even before they were distributed to regular bookstores (publishers usually send advance copies of their books to reviewers well before the official publication date), other reviewers got the same idea. With the encouragement of the Strand, reviewers from New York City, the book capital of the United States, began to descend upon the store every week with arms, boxes, and automobile trunks filled with those books they did not or could not review or those that they did not care to keep. The Strand proved to be a ready buyer and their customers soon realized that they could purchase almost any new book published—from bestsellers to less known but equally coveted volumes—for 50 percent off the retail price. Since then, every day, hordes of buyers now scour and scan the review tables and sections (consisting of 10,000 books at any given time, with new titles coming in daily, a virtual bookstore within a bookstore), looking for current works at half of what they cost uptown or at other stores.

The Strand was founded over fifty years ago by Benjamin Bass, who, during the Depression, had tried a variety of jobs, from construction worker to salesman, without success. Out of desperation he opened his own bookstore. "I was quite a reader and I thought owning a bookstore would be an easy and good way to earn a living. I thought I'd be able to sit down all day, read good books and discuss literature and philosophy with my customers. I learned immediately that to make any money

137

from a bookstore, you must work at it *constantly*. I've hardly sat down since I opened."

Today, the store is managed by Ben's son, Fred, who travels all over the world to buy books for his store and is a partner in six remainder stores in London. "It's a disease," says Fred about his bookbuying habits. "I get an attack, something like a panic, of book buying. I simply *must* keep fresh used books flowing over my shelves. And every day the clerks weed out the unsalable stuff from the shelves and bins and we throw it out. *Tons* of dead books go out nightly. And *I* bought 'em! But I just have to make room for fresh stock to keep the shelves lively."

In addition to new, used, remaindered, and review books, the Strand has a special floor consisting entirely of rare books. Here in a less hectic atmosphere than the street or basement floors one can buy a first edition of Boswell's *Life of Samuel Johnson* (1791) worth thousands; a two-volume facsimile of the Gutenberg Bible (of only three hundred printed) selling for $5,000; the nine-volume edition of *Tristram Shandy* for $1,250; an illuminated incunabulum from 1473 for $2,000; or Picasso's *Lysistrata*, with his signature, for $1,200.

Since Bass is continually buying books to add to the store's stocks, there are boxes and boxes of books located on another floor, yet to be opened for shelving. As Donald Newlove described it in his article on the Strand in *New York* magazine: "This floor is *huge*—it is a Great Plains of books, like Charles Foster Kane's cellar, far shelves vanishing into alcoves, waves of marked boxes bought from private collectors, a Thames or Mississippi of human spirit transfigured into printer's ink."

The Strand issues book catalogs and lists of all kinds, and book lovers can be placed on the mailing list simply by writing to the store and mentioning the kinds of books in which they are interested. Although they do not accept credit cards, the Strand will take personal checks, with proper identification.

Friday afternoons and Saturdays are the busiest days for the Strand, when at some points there are over five hundred customers in the store at one time. "You couldn't read all the titles, even if you tried," says Bass of his millions of books. "But I defy anyone who is really interested in books to come in here and *not* find a book that captures his interest and fascination."

828 Broadway, New York, New York 10003; Tel. 212-GR 3-1452; Hours: Monday–Saturday, 9:30 A.M.–6:30 P.M.

WOMANBOOKS

NEW YORK
NEW YORK

A small woman, elegantly dressed, browses next to her blue-jeaned daughter. The mother picks up a copy of *The Managerial Woman* and then goes on to something else, while the daughter, unaware of the world, reads *The Hite Report*. Two young women study the bulletin board and heatedly discuss something they find there. A young man with a backpack scans and browses the poetry section. The scene is a typical tableau from Womanbooks, one of the growing number of, and one of the best, feminist bookstores in the United States.

Started as a contributive way to earn a living that would also be a pleasant occupation, the store is owned and operated cooperatively by Karyn London, Fabi Romero Oak, and Eleanor Batchelder; the three women share the work equally—from keeping up the inventory to sweeping the floors. There is no specialization as to task and no status as to who is the "boss."

Womanbooks does much more than just sell books. It serves as an information center, where both visiting and local women can find out things such as where to locate a good divorce lawyer or a sympathetic gynecologist, how to locate a consciousness-raising group, where to find a job, the names of the best child-care centers in the area. There is an extensive,

139

organized bulletin board and notebooks filled with information on resources for women. The store has become an obligatory stop for anyone coming from women's centers elsewhere in the country. All kinds of women come to Womanbooks, however, not just those who are politically active, and the store caters to a broad cross-section of both radical and neighborhood types. Since many of the women who live on New York's Upper West Side work with words, as editors, writers, publishers, they are aware of the movement and have begun to use the store as an ideological and practical base.

The store's sections include sports, women's studies, psychology, health, private life, aging, "herstory," women and the revolution, and others. One of the most extensive sections is on childbirth and child-care. The shop carries books by and about men, except in the poetry and fiction sections, where all of the books are by female authors. There are many books which are not necessarily profitable but are of political value and of which the store might sell only one or two a year. There is also an extensive magazine and small press collection, where it's possible to get a full range of publications available hardly anywhere else, such as *Big Mama Rag*, *Lesbian Tide*, or a Jewish women's literary magazine.

The range of activities sponsored by the store is too broad to describe or even list in detail but includes, in part, poetry readings, softball games, parties, sing-alongs, dance concerts, children's hours, lectures, discussions, and seminars.

As someone described it: "The store gives women the feeling that they are important, challenging, exciting."

201 West 92nd Street, New York, New York 10025; Tel. 212-873-4121. Hours: Tuesday–Saturday, 10:00 A.M.–7:00 P.M.; Sunday, 12 Noon–6:00 P.M.

A house without books is like a house without windows.
                                                    HORACE MANN

Bloomingdale's really *is* one of the most glamorous stores in the world. It was the only nonofficial stop made by Queen Elizabeth on her historic visit to New York, and it serves as a well-known gathering place and posh shopping headquarters for Manhattan's affluent East Side cognoscenti.

The book department is a further reflection of the store's chic mystique: Bookstalls is certainly the most interesting and magical book section of any department store in New York City. Profusely stocked with current hardcovers, mass-market best sellers, and high-quality paperbacks, all attractively displayed, the department also has a superb cookbook section, a strong selection of travel books, and one of the best collections of art, architecture, designing, and fashion books of any bookstore in the city. Where else but in Bloomingdale's could the book, *New York on $500 a Day*, sell "hundreds and hundreds of copies," according to Lois Keiner, the department's manager and buyer, who looks as though she herself had stepped from the pages of *Vogue*. In fact, while browsing in Bookstalls, it is usually difficult to tell who is the salesclerk, the customer, the celebrity: this all adds to the excitement and mystery of shopping at the store. Barbra Streisand was in Bookstalls last December and practically bought out the department to send books as Christmas gifts to her friends. Recently, Craig Claiborne, James Beard, and Lady Harlech each whipped up a personal gourmet delight in Bookstalls as a sample of what one can learn from any one of their respective cookbooks. Jacqueline Onassis is a "constant browser and buyer," according to the salespeople, as are Woody Allen, Cliff Robertson, Tricia Cox, and Shirley MacLaine. Authors give autographings frequently throughout the year—Edwin Newman and Eric Sevareid have been in the store lately—and there are even

141

such events as wine tastings (John Lindsay was guest of honor at one) to introduce a new encyclopedia of the grape. It is not unknown for elegantly dressed customers to come to Bookstalls, buy several hundred dollars' worth of books, and then have them delivered to their waiting limousines—or to an address in St. Moritz, Monte Carlo, Southampton, or Palm Springs. Sometimes a uniformed, French-speaking governess will wander into the department with her charge, who will then invariably sit in front of the children's section, paging through books until its mother returns from shopping in another part of the store.

Located on the "7½th" floor (take the escalator to seven and look for the signs) in a large, separate niche, above and totally removed from the rest of the floor, Bookstalls has an intimate library atmosphere, and after a few minutes of browsing, it's difficult to remember that one is inside a department store.

In addition to books, there are some unusual items to be found in Bookstalls. It carries a line of clever canvas and fabric tote bags, designed and made exclusively for Bloomingdale's. The large tan book bag, imprinted "Heavy Reading," is presumably for hefty tomes. A small companion bag, which proclaims "Light Reading," is perfect for paperbacks. There are also totes with the imprint of the New York City Ballet, the Broadway shows *Annie* and *Dracula*, and one that simply says, "Bloomingdale's." Bookstalls also sells "cover-ups," small canvas book covers used primarily to preserve and make paperback covers more attractive.

Bookstalls will special order any book that has been published within the year and will—and does—mail books anyplace in the world. The shop also gladly fills mail orders.

Says Ms. Keiner, of Bookstalls: "We have a real bookstore—in every sense of the word—in the heart of a great department store. People come here to find books and they usually come away with something, since our philosophy of bookselling is to carry a good quality assortment of something for everybody."

Please note that Joseph Thorndike's *The Very Rich* was one of the big sellers in Bookstalls.

But why, after all, in a city filled with bookstores, should you seek out one in the midst of a department store? Simply because, in addition to stocking a large and excellent selection of titles, Bookstalls also carries the ambience of Bloomingdale's, with all the fascination with celebrities and unexpected surprises that that conveys.

Bloomingdale's (7½ Floor), 59th St. and 3rd Avenue, New York, New York 10022; Tel. 212-223-7570. Hours: Monday–Saturday, 9:40 A.M.–6:00 P.M.; Thursday till 9:00 P.M.

QUINION BOOKS

NEW YORK
NEW YORK

Quinion Books, founded in 1976, is located on the fringes of Greenwich Village not far from the White Horse Tavern, a literary landmark of sorts, since Dylan Thomas used to while away the hours there drinking his stout and ale. The store specializes exclusively in drama and in cookbooks, including many foreign-language books in these areas. How many books? There are usually three to four thousand in stock at any given time, and if you're interested, you can be placed on their mailing list by writing to them.

Because people in all walks of life are interested in cooking or in recipes, and certainly in theater, the clientele is most diverse. Personal service is the keynote, and if you have a taste for an authentic foreign recipe, chances are that you'll find it here. Jesse Feiler, owner of Quinion, seems to be thoroughly familiar with all his books and enjoys discussing them, so if you *are* in the mood for one of grandma's dishes (whether your grandmother happens to come from Japan, Norway, Italy, or Vermont), the store can probably help you find it, in its original form and in its original language.

Credit cards—all credit cards—are welcome here, and so will you be. It's a friendly store. You'll find Quinion Books to be airy and spacious, very well organized, and well lit. It's a nice place to shop and find a moment of quiet, browsing through the unusual and well-stocked shelves.

Because the shop offers free mailing, and because it services mail orders, it would be worth getting on the mailing list to learn about new acquisitions. But expect something unusual. This is the only store we know of that specializes in two such vertical areas, and then puts the icing on the cake by specializing further in foreign-language books on these subjects.

541 Hudson Street, New York, New York 10014; Tel. 212-989-6130. Hours: seven days a week, 12:00 Noon till 10:00 P.M.

RIZZOLI INTERNATIONAL BOOKSTORE   NEW YORK NEW YORK

Rizzoli was founded in 1909 by Angelo Rizzoli in Milan as a small printing operation. Now, almost seventy years later, the company remains family-owned, under the direction of the founder's grandson and namesake, Angelo Rizzoli, but it has expanded enormously to include ventures on four continents, ranging from book, magazine, and newspaper publishing to film production and distribution, ink and paper manufacturing, printing, real estate development, and tourism. *La Dolce Vita*, *Juliet of the Spirits*, and *8-1/2* are Rizzoli films. Oriana Fallaci, John Updike, Kurt Vonnegut, John Hersey, Arthur Miller, and Tennessee Williams are among the numerous writers published in Italian by Rizzoli, reported to be the fifth or sixth largest publisher in the world. Rizzoli publishes and distributes the largest daily newspaper in Italy, *Corriere della Sera*, as well as the mass-circulation magazines, *Oggi* and *L'Europeo*, and the Italian edition of *Playboy*—altogether, 40 percent of the print media in Italy.

Rizzoli first came to the United States in 1964, when its elegant Fifth Avenue bookstore was opened. It quickly became famous as one of the most beautiful bookstores in America, with its fine wood paneling, marble floors, floor to ceiling mirrors, and imported wrought-iron chandeliers. It also became known as an invaluable source of foreign-language newspapers, magazines, books and records; even in a city as cosmopolitan as New York, no other bookstore carried as many different languages—the Rizzoli selection was tops and still is. Exquisitely illustrated art books are also a specialty of the store: if a book is beautiful, chances are Rizzoli carries it. And finally, to New Yorkers "in the know," Rizzoli became the favorite meeting place of celebrities: Jacqueline Onassis, Ansel Adams, Rudolf Nureyev, Norman Mailer, and many others have shopped at Rizzoli from the very beginning. They still do.

When pianists such as Claudia Arrau or Arthur Rubinstein come into the store, their records are always placed on the phonograph and their music-making wafts through the store. Couples dressed in evening clothes often come in before or after dinner to browse. Rizzoli might simply be the most romantic bookstore in America.

In addition to books, there is an art gallery and a tiny, underground theater, used for small private showings by the nation's film-makers. It is one of the plushest, most attractive screening rooms in New York.

Rizzoli decided to expand its American operations in 1975. New stores have opened in Chicago, Atlanta, downtown New York on Union Square, and Georgetown, and more are planned. Future locations will include Boston, Miami, Houston, Beverly Hills, and Toronto, over a period of about five years. Rizzoli has also expanded by founding an American-based publishing house, called Rizzoli International Publications, Inc., with a specialization in art books, although they've also published some excellent music books (Schubert, Wagner, and Mahler). In just two years, Rizzoli's list included more than one hundred books. A catalog is available on request.

The third "arm" of the expansion program was to sell foreign-language books, wholesale, to libraries, schools, and other bookstores. This program has been enormously successful.

The old-world ambience and European elegance of Rizzoli marks it as one of the most attractive bookstores in America. Book lovers have found and will continue to find it to be one of their favorite browsing experiences.

712 Fifth Avenue, New York, New York 10019; Tel. 212-397-3706. Hours: Monday–Saturday, 9:30 A.M.–7:00 P.M.; magazine section, until 8:00 P.M.

THE SCIENCE FICTION SHOP

NEW YORK NEW YORK

Step into a small rocket-ship-like room, with rounded modules and books lining all of the walls. All of the volumes concern space, the future, the fantasy of men both from earth and from other planets. No, it's not the library of the *Enterprise*, it's the Science Fiction Bookshop, one of the best all science-fiction and fantasy bookstores in the world.

Obviously, the store carries such authors as Asimov, Heinlein, Arthur C. Clarke, and Ray Bradbury, but it's also possible to get such hard-to-find items as old copies of *Amazing Stores*, obscure and somewhat esoteric journals published in limited numbers, out-of-print and scarce science-fiction books, both hardbound and paperback.

Founded in 1973 by Baird Searles and Martin Last, the Science Fiction Bookshop is the unofficial center for SF and fantasy lovers of New York City and surrounding areas. A bulletin board lists the science-fiction films that will be appearing on television and in the theaters that week, as well as other

146

information such as special lectures and meetings of the Science Fiction Society. The local television stations often send a crew to the Science Fiction Shop after a moon-shot or a Mars landing to solicit opinions and reactions; and the store is used constantly by the media as a reference library, since most public libraries are weak in the area of science fiction.

There are some five thousand titles in print at the store—and many of these are listed in the catalog, which is available free of charge by request in person or by mail. The store will search for out-of-print books and special order any book in print.

As to additional services and events, the store is constantly promoting one activity or another: author autograph parties, lectures, science-fiction writers' workshops, seminars on science-fiction history. Almost every famous science-fiction writer has visited the store, including Arthur C. Clarke, who orders books to be sent to his home in Sri Lanka.

One of the owners summed up the general feeling about the store: "We seem to be an idea whose time has come."

56 Eighth Avenue, New York, New York 10014; Tel. 212-741-0270. Hours: Monday–Friday, 11:00 A.M.–8:00 P.M.; Saturday, 11:00 A.M.–6:00 P.M.; Sunday, 12:00 Noon–6:00 P.M.

A. BUSCHKE   NEW YORK
                                                NEW YORK

When Abraham Lincoln made his well-known Cooper Union address, he stayed at a hotel located on the corner of Eleventh Street and Broadway. That hotel is now an office building, and on the sixth floor are the shop and offices of A. Buschke, bookseller. The stock consists of a sea of some 80,000 to 100,000 books crammed into six separate rooms and quite easily wins the "most cluttered bookstore in America" grand prize. Mr. Buschke seems to know where everything is, however, and customers who have patience will be rewarded with his literary treasures. The store has two specialties, chess and Russian scholarly periodicals, and supplies collectors and libraries from all over the world with titles from either of these categories. Sometimes, the two areas overlap, as in a full run of the first Russian chess magazine (started in 1859), which is available for $350.00.

Bobby Fischer used to spend time browsing and buying books at the store, and when he won the U.S. championship, at the age of fourteen, was given a gift certificate by Mr. Buschke. "Most youngsters would have walked off with an armful of books right then," says Buschke, "but Fischer came back for a year and picked nothing but the best."

Arturo Toscanini once browsed in the store and paid for a $3.00 book by giving Buschke a $100 bill.

Occasionally, Buschke issues lists of his chess books for sale, and anyone can be placed on his mailing list by writing to him at the store. The lists are crammed full of scarce, out-of-print, and rare chess books and are virtual collector's items in themselves. His holdings in Russian periodicals are too extensive to catalog, but libraries and collectors who are missing certain numbers are almost sure to find what they want by writing to him.

Mr. Buschke will do as much as possible to satisfy the requests of his customers, but is forthright about his dislike of browsers who only come to him for information. He sends them to libraries. But where else will they find out what opening Lasker played in his final match game against Steinitz—and in Russian?

80 East 11th Street (Suite 623-627), New York, New York 10003; Tel. 212-254-2555. Hours: Monday and Friday only, 10:30 A.M.–1:30 P.M.; other times by appointment.

Reading is to the mind what exercise is to the body.
SIR RICHARD STEELE

THE GOTHAM
BOOK MART

NEW YORK
NEW YORK

Probably no other American bookstore is so intertwined with the development of modern literature as is the Gotham Book Mart. It has also served for over a half a century as a meeting place in New York City for some of the most renowned authors and poets of the day. The history of Gotham Book Mart represents the virtual history of contemporary American letters, and its founder, Frances Steloff, has assumed the unofficial mantle of patron saint of writers everywhere. The store has become, as author Letty Cottin Pogrebin described it in the *New York Times*, "an honest-to-goodness shrine."

When in Europe, Henry Miller kept up a lengthy correspondence with Frances, and her purchases of his banned books kept him in pocket—and sometimes more—money during a time when he really needed it.

Tennessee Williams was once a clerk in the store but was fired for coming in late all the time.

The first thing Dame Edith Sitwell did when visiting from London was to stop at the Gotham Book Mart.

Gertrude Stein once came in to check on the sales of her books.

Christopher Morley, Buckminster Fuller, and William Rose Benét often met in the garden behind the store to have lunch, which they would invariably bring in brown bags.

"My customers educated my tastes," says Mrs. Steloff, who started the store in 1920 with some borrowed money, less than two hundred dollars, and very little formal education. Her own tastes ran to metaphysics and the occult, with such authors as Gurdjieff, Ouspensky, and Krishnamurti—but through the preferences of the writers who frequented the store, it soon became known as the center for the avant-garde.

She promoted and carried the controversial works of Ezra Pound, James Joyce, and Henry Miller in the days when it was difficult, sometimes illegal, to secure and sell them; but she showed faith in the avant-garde, and her store became internationally known as a result.

The authors who came to the Gotham Book Mart to shop, browse, give readings, or just stop by to talk to Frances Steloff comprise a literary pantheon. A partial listing, other than those already mentioned: W. H. Auden, Allen Ginsberg, J. D. Salinger, Brendan Behan, Thornton Wilder, Jean Cocteau, Dylan Thomas, Gore Vidal, Norman Mailer, Stephen Spender, Anaïs Nin, Marianne Moore, Padraic Colum, Edmund Wilson, E. E. Cummings, H. L. Mencken.

The store, which is below street level and is marked by a sign, "Wise Men Fish Here," is delightfully cluttered in a Dickensian way—books are piled everywhere, photographs of Joyce, Pound, Hemingway, and other great writers hang from the walls. There are classic, almost heroic, sections of poetry, drama, fiction.

In the 1930s there was a carton in the front of the store bearing the inscription, "Help Henry Miller." Miller had written to the store saying that he was returning broke from Europe. Soon, people began putting in canned goods, used clothing, vitamins, and a thermos bottle. Miller was grateful when he eventually arrived in the store and retrieved his booty.

Aside from helping authors and selling books for most of her life, Frances Steloff has also been instrumental in getting books published or reprinted, as the following witty and memorable correspondence in 1950 between her and Random House's publisher, the late Bennett Cerf, indicates (*Journal of Modern Literature* 4[April 1975]):

Dear Bennett:
    This is to serve notice that you will not have peace or rest until you promise to reprint *Absalom, Absalom*. We have been advertising for many months without receiving a single quotation. Now at last I get the enclosed [a quotation from a dealer offering it at $74.25].

I called the guy up just to see if he was serious, and sure enough the 25¢ is for postage and insurance, he explains, rare books must be insured. The last copy we sold for $20.00 and I thought we were robbing the poor customer, but there is no other way to lay hands on this title.

We have a poor student in Germany who made great sacrifices to get $7.50 to us; about six months ago we thought we could supply one at that price. And so we keep on searching without success. It is as you must know the most important of all Faulkner titles, and Faulkner has been on the up and up for the last two years.

Will you not take my word for it that it will be the best selling title in the Modern Library for a very long time. I had hoped to avoid annoying you and thought I would extract a promise from Saxe [Commins?] but he passed the buck.

With love and Easter greetings.

Always,
Frances

P.S. I have just finished nagging Knopf into saying they will immediately reprint *If It Die*, do you remember?

Dear Frances:

Thanks for your note about *Absalom, Absalom*, and I am impressed to see a price of $74.25 quoted for a copy thereof.

We most certainly are going to put this book in the Modern Library, but that won't be until the Fall of 1951. This Fall we are doing *Light in August* in the Modern Library. We are also doing a volume of Faulkner's collected short stories as a Random House publication. Eventually, every line that Faulkner has ever written will be back in print.

In short, my dear, I ask you only to keep your pants on, which is certainly something I wouldn't have told a girl twenty years ago. Time marches on, God damn it.

Love,
Bennett

Dear Bennett:

Thanks for your prompt reply, but am I satisfied? I should say not.

Why do you publish *Light in August* which is available from New Directions ahead of *Absalom, Absalom* which is scarcer than hen's teeth, and far more in demand because it is his best title.

I never could understand why publishers behave the way they do,

151

but you used to be different. I wish I had the time to make up a list of the Sins of Publishers.

Love as usual,
Frances

Recently, New Mexico State University at Las Cruces bought virtually half the stock of the store—little poetry magazines from the 1920s and 1930s, esoteric novels, obscure or long-forgotten literary criticisms—for $485,000, one of the largest single sales in bookselling history. It is now called the Frances Steloff Rare Book Collection.

Today the store, now owned by Andreas Brown, is totally restocked and still carries avant-garde books and journals, modern fiction, and an enormous film and drama section. And, it is still as cluttered as ever. As someone once said, the Gotham Book Mart is the only "real" bookstore in New York City and God help the one who organizes the clutter.

41 West 47th St., New York, New York 10036; Tel. 212-PL7-0367. Hours: Monday–Saturday, 9:30 A.M.–6:30 P.M.

THE DRAMA BOOK SHOP   NEW YORK NEW YORK

Shortly after Ellen Burstyn won both the Academy and Tony awards, she spent four hours browsing in the Drama Book Shop. None of the customers took notice of her, perhaps because they, too, are actors or actresses involved in their own careers. The shop is often visited by the famous or soon-to-be famous in search of material about the theater, and usually no one gives anyone else a second glance.

Tucked away atop a five-story office building in mid-town Manhattan, the Drama Book Shop is the country's only bookstore to specialize exclusively in theater, and it has been in operation for over a half-century. Co-owner Arthur Seelen and Allen S. Collins have, according to a recent article in the *New York Times*, "encyclopedic knowledge" of the theater. "Arthur Seelen is one of the world's leading experts on drama." He makes buying trips abroad "to keep ahead of the cognoscenti" and keeps himself constantly apprised of developments in theater today. This dedication reflects itself in the stock carried by the store, a superb amalgam of what anyone interested in theater, from scholar to professional, could possibly want.

As a result, the store is always peopled by actors, actresses, technicians, playwrights, and students of the theater, all of whom buy, browse, or use the store as combination reference library and social gathering place.

The store carries almost every play currently in print, an enormous film section, and books on theater criticism, lighting technique, costuming, and pronunciation and voice projection. The store does an extensive mail-order business through its annotated bibliography, which is mailed quarterly to six thousand customers here and abroad. Although it does not list all of the books carried by the Drama Book Shop, it contains information on new theater books and peripheral subjects, such as finishing furniture for people in set production and design.

Several years ago, the Drama Book Shop started publishing its own titles under the imprint of Drama Book Specialists, its major title to date being *Performing Arts Books in Print* by Ralph Newman Schoolcraft.

Mainly because of the upsurge of interest in community theater, after fifty years of bookselling the Drama Book Shop still prospers: in 1977 its gross sales were close to three-quarters of a million dollars.

150 West 52nd St., New York, New York 10019; Tel. 212-582-1037. Hours: Monday–Friday, 9:30 A.M.–6:00 P.M.; Saturday, 1:00 P.M.– 5:00 P.M.

HACKER ART BOOKS

The new revised and enlarged edition of *Paul Cézanne: Letters*; *The Cross: Its History and Symbolism*, by George Willard Benson; Adolf Mahr's *Christian Art in Ancient Ireland*; *The Architecture of the Renaissance in France*, by W. H. Ward; *Ko-Ji Ho-Ten: Dictionnaire à L'Usage des Amateurs et Collectionneurs d'Objets d'Art Japonais et Chinois*; Paul S. Wingert's *American Indian Sculpture: A Study of the Northwest Coast*. The list goes on, and on, and gloriously on, for Hacker Art Books may well be the largest art bookstore in the world, with more than 100,000 books on every imaginable aspect of art. The books are old, new, and some extremely rare and valuable. They range in price from a $2.95 paperback to a single volume worth thousands of dollars.

Seymour Hacker founded his store forty years ago, and in the interim has gained the respect of art historians and experts for his own expertise in this area. "I probably know more about art books than anyone in the world," he says softly, and it could be so. Librarians frequently phone him for advice and appraisals of rare books they're thinking of acquiring. He himself travels all over the world, examining books, importing them, then selling them directly through his shop, or acting as distributor for other art stores.

Many of the books are sold to libraries, colleges, and universities throughout the country, and to do this Hacker has invented an unusual system. He sends three bookmobiles, each carrying about one thousand books that are representative of his stock, to visit the schools and libraries: two go to establishments in the eastern states, and the other visits the western states. Librarians are thus given the opportunity to see, handle, and assess the kinds of books they might want to order. The process avoids costly returns, and it keeps Hacker and his

154

highly knowledgeable staff (some of whom have worked for him for fifteen years) in touch with what kinds of books are wanted.

The store carries books on all of the fine and applied arts. There's a small section on film, theater, and visual design. Largely because of customers' requests, there is an extensive collection of books on primitive and African art, particularly the art of Nigeria—as well, of course, as the numerous books on European art of many ages. The collection on modern art, especially American art, is also extensive.

Within this specialized store there is a specialization: books on costume and scene design. Hacker owns the largest collection of costume books in the world, and the books on scene design are as extensive. This collection often attracts visits by the best working designers, many of whom are friends of Hacker's, as they are researching particular periods in order to create new costumes or sets. For example, the store's remarkable collection of turn-of-the-century books on architecture and design became the basis for the design of the sets for *A Little Night Music*.

This is a wonderful store for the student or amateur, as well as the expert. The highly knowledgeable staff can recommend books on a customer's general area of interest or give highly technical guidance in the comparative values of antiquarian books. The store will search for books requested by a customer and special order them as necessary. The staff prepares catalogs three times a year, and interested customers can request that they be put on the mailing list. Twice a year, in the fall and spring, special sales are held and books may be sold for up to 50 percent off.

Hacker also reprints selected titles. Often, they are excellent books that have gone out of print. Seymour Hacker selects the books and frequently has an authority in the field add a new introduction and, sometimes, additional material, making the reprint, at times, a more valuable resource than the original book.

155

Perhaps it's because of the magnificent collection of rare books; perhaps it's because of the works of art that grace most of the books' covers; but whatever the reason, Hacker Art Books has something of the ambience of a museum—a museum which happens to sell its extraordinary wares.

54 West 57th Street, New York, New York 10019; Tel. 212-757-1450. Hours: Monday–Saturday, 9:00 A.M.–6:00 P.M.

BRENTANO'S

**NEW YORK
NEW YORK**

Brentano's is one of the most respected names in American bookselling, although its motto, "Booksellers to the World," is certainly additionally appropriate. It has long been a favorite browsing place for knowledgeable New Yorkers and visitors. In addition to its vast selection of books—from old and rare to best sellers—the store is the testing ground for innovative merchandise and has been the birthplace for many new trends in arts and ideas. Brentano's was the first major retailer of its type to feature original art, the first to carry a collection of rare seashells. The game of Scrabble made its debut there; so did the popular joke gift, the Pet Rock. And the history of the store is fascinating.

In 1853, August Brentano, an Austrian immigrant, opened a newsstand in front of the old New York Hotel in lower Manhattan. His key to success was his running speed. Noting that guests were betting on the English races and boxing matches, Brentano ordered newspapers from England, met the ships in port, and rushed the latest results back to his stand, which soon became the established place where bets were settled. Business prospered. (Legend has it that Brentano was known as "the bookie," and this is possibly the derivation of that term.) Soon Brentano's moved up—and indoors—to the hallway of the Revere House at Broadway and Houston. Above the table, which now offered books as well as newspapers, the sign read "Brentano's Literary Emporium." Within a few years August had a real emporium, starting in a basement room but soon occupying half the building at 708 Broadway. Because of its unique stock of foreign books and periodicals, Brentano's became a rendezvous for European visitors and cosmopolitan New Yorkers. When it moved to 33 Union Square, just down the block from Tiffany's, it was already a landmark. Sightseers came to gape at the browsers, who included Charles Dickens, Ralph Waldo Emerson, James Russell Lowell, Lillian Russell, John Drew, and Ulysses S. Grant.

August doubled his staff when he hired his fifteen-year-old nephew, Arthur. Arthur became a store institution, selling books from the floor for the next seventy years. His courtly manners and impeccable dress set the tone for the entire store. Arthur personally saw to it that all Brentano's employees boasted smartly starched collars, shined shoes, and unlimited courtesy. He was also responsible for inaugurating the old and rare books department.

In 1879, Brentano's became a publisher, putting out magazines on field and water sports and chess. Later came *Book Chat*, a magazine about books and authors. Brentano's was the first to print the plays of George Bernard Shaw in this country, as well as the controversial works on birth control by Margaret Sanger. The publishing interests were sold in the 1930s.

Brentano's became known as "Booksellers to the World" for a unique service. The store would scour the market to locate any publication requested, no matter when or where published. Orders came in from around the globe, and the business gained international prominence.

Burned out by a fire in 1898, Brentano's emerged a bigger and better store. The gala reopening had a surprise star when it was interrupted by a casual book-buying visit from Admiral

Dewey, fresh from his triumph as the hero of Manila. The opening was forgotten as clerks and police fought to hold back autograph hunters.

Shortly after the turn of the century, Brentano's followed the carriage trade uptown to Twenty-seventh Street. Customers now included Andrew Carnegie, J. P. Morgan, and Henry Clay Frick. It was in this store some years later that another mob scene occurred when Gertrude Stein appeared for an autographing party and was besieged by fans.

In the mid-1920s, again following the fashionable, Brentano's moved to its present quarters at 586 Fifth Avenue, between Forty-seventh and Forty-eighth streets, where it continued to meet all types of requests with unfailing dedication—including an order for forty-two feet of books in shades of green to match a customer's color scheme. Cruise ship passengers were a prime market for reading matter during this era. Store president Arthur Brentano, Jr., reported in 1928 that the store had delivered some twenty thousand books to one ocean liner alone during the year.

In the 1930s, hard hit by the depression, the Brentano family sold its interests to Stanton Griffis, who later served as U.S. ambassador to Poland, Egypt, Argentina, and Spain. Under his aegis, the store prospered once again. Stocks were expanded to include records, stamps, coins, and films. Stanton's son, Nixon, became president of Brentano's. He refurbished the New York store, began using modern window displays, and replaced the old hand ledgers with mechanized bookkeeping, much to the dismay of the clerks, who felt they were losing personal touch with their customers. In the 1950s, history was made when Brentano's became the first important bookstore to put in a department of paperback books. Today paperbacks occupy an entire floor of the store. Brentano's caused additional shock waves in New York art circles by introducing a bookstore gallery of original art. Despite established dealers' initial fears that this would ruin the art business, the move, now

158

widely copied, is credited with helping create an entire new market for art. The store also began to sell reproductions of museum-owned sculpture and jewelry, items previously available only in scattered museum shops.

It was in the early 1960s that Brentano's was acquired by MacMillan, Inc., a corporation whose interests include instruction, art, educational materials, music, films, and periodicals as well as books. Brentano's continued to pioneer the concept of the bookstore as a center for many arts. Stocks were expanded to include the best arts and crafts from many lands, artifacts and antiquities and other unusual merchandise not generally available. The New York store was then enlarged to double its floor space, and set up as a series of galleries to properly showcase its diversified offerings. A favorite new browsing corner was Fun and Games, featuring a renowned selection of chess sets and the very latest in sophisticated adult games and puzzles. Scrabble was launched here.

During the past decade, Brentano's activities and innovations have been both remarkable and newsworthy. "Tonight at Eight," a continuing Thursday night series, was inaugurated. Its varied offerings, ranging from chamber music to fencing exhibits to a Japanese tea ceremony, earned a wide following—as well as an award to Brentano's from the New York Board of Trade for fostering the arts.

Brentano's literally rolled out a red carpet in front of the store for a "show-biz" gala celebrating publication of Elia Kazan's first novel, *The Arrangement*. Cohosts included Robert Anderson, Archibald MacLeish, John Steinbeck, William Inge, Budd Schulberg, Thornton Wilder, and Tennessee Williams. Guests sipped champagne among the bookstacks and dined on lobster curry and beef stroganoff in the rare book department.

A new decorating trend began when Brentano's introduced its Art in Nature boutique, featuring shells, minerals, butterflies, and other examples of nature's creations. Once,

Maurice Chevalier dropped by to autograph some books—and more than a thousand customers and three TV crews followed. Sore-handed but game, the debonair Frenchman spent the following day closeted in his hotel room filling autograph requests for those who had been left out the day before.

One of New York's first American Indian crafts shops was introduced at Brentano's, with two days of events that included demonstrations of fine Indian sculpting, stone carving, painting, doll making, singing, and dancing. Kite flying also soared that year when Brentano's new Kite Corner inspired scores of new enthusiasts into the city's parks.

Brentano's also began to sell artifacts from New Guinea— masks, ancestral plaques, and hunting charms representing the everyday and religious life of the natives were introduced to New York at Brentano's. Other innovative merchandise: wind chimes, rare seaforms, and Russian carvings from the Ural Mountains region.

Recently, Brentano's became a publisher once again for one special edition, scooping the entire industry with the first complete private publication of Richard Nixon's White House tapes. And the store has influenced publishing in other ways. An obscure business book recently became a national best seller when Brentano's vice-president and veteran book-buyer Lillian Friedman spotted a mail-order ad for Robert J. Ringer's *Winning through Intimidation*. Initially printed by the author himself, the book took off after Brentano's began its own ad campaign; publication of *WTI* was soon taken on by a major publishing house.

Noontime in the store can be a lively affair. Shoppers may meet such celebrity authors as Dan Rather, Gore Vidal, Theodore White, Joseph Heller, or John Lindsay appearing to autograph their books—or see Zuñi dancers, Israeli ceramists, or Indian kite-makers demonstrating their special skills. Famous customers of Brentano's have included major literary, social, and cultural figures of more than a century past. Among them: the Queen of Egypt, King Carol of Rumania, Lord Beaverbrook, Irish prime minister Eamon de Valera, French premier Paul Reynaud, James Joyce, Rudyard Kipling, Ernest Hemingway, Gertrude Stein, Lillian Russell, General Pershing, Alice Longworth, Eva LeGalliene, the Duke and Duchess of Windsor, and Israeli prime minister David Ben-Gurion. Today's shoppers, too, may find themselves browsing next to such celebrities as Paul Newman, Cary Grant, Gene Shalit, Irving Wallace, or Jacqueline Onassis, all of whom shop at the store.

Since 1965 Brentano's has opened nineteen stores in a major development program that has also seen the New York Fifth Avenue flagship store double in size and the historic Washington, D.C., store triple its space in a move to quarters in the National Press Building. Other openings included Hartford, Connecticut; Boston and Chestnut Hill, Massachusetts; Hyattsville and Chevy Chase, Maryland; New York's Greenwich Village and the New York suburbs of White Plains, Manhasset, Queens, and Massapequa. On the West Coast, Brentano's San Francisco store has been joined by four new California locations since 1972. The past five years have also seen a Southern expansion into Atlanta, New Orleans, and Dallas, as well as the first Midwest store, in St. Louis.

Brentano's on F Street in Washington, D.C., has been an institution since it was first opened in 1885. Every president since Theodore Roosevelt has been a customer. Two outstanding examples of Brentano's custom binding work were done for presidents: Theodore Roosevelt's famous "Pigskin Library," bound to withstand climatic conditions in Africa, and a special presentation set of art books given to Dwight D. Eisenhower by his cabinet on his second inauguration.

In over one hundred years of bookselling, Brentano's has managed to emerge as one of the great bookstores of the world, and possibly the greatest in history.

586 Fifth Avenue, New York, New York 10036; Tel. 212-757-8600.
Hours: Monday, Tuesday, Wednesday, Friday, 9:45 A.M.–6:45 P.M.;
Thursday, 9:45 A.M.–8:00 P.M.; Saturday, 9:45 A.M.–6:00 P.M.

THE SCRIBNER BOOK STORE   NEW YORK NEW YORK

One hundred years ago, when New York's Fifth Avenue was crowded with horse-drawn carriages, footmen would graciously and gently help customers into Scribner's so that they could buy or browse for books. In addition to an efficient staff with impeccable manners, the shop itself was elegant: wrought-iron railings, high columns, skylights, carpeting over hardwood floors, blue and white ceilings—all housed in a building originally designed to be one thing and one thing only, a bookstore, and an exemplary example of the architecture of the period.

Today, the horse-drawn carriages, for the most part, are gone, but a great deal has remained the same at Scribner's: it is still one of the most beautiful bookstores in the country.

Igor Kropotkin, president of Scribner's, told us: "We like to think we have style. We also like to think we give maximum service. Most of our sales people have sufficient knowledge to complete this triangle. That's what the store is all about."

The store—which boasts a staff of fifty—carries upwards of forty thousand new hardcover and paperback titles and has probably the best collection of art books of any general bookstore in New York. It has an enormous inventory of children's books, travel books, cookbooks, and business and professional books. There is also a small but excellent stock of books with leather bindings, which are done in England and shipped to New York periodically.

162

Scribner's boasts a very fine collection of "standard authors," from Jane Austen to Joseph Heller and from Dorothy Sayers to Leo Tolstoy, all in hardbound (although many of the same books are duplicated in paper), for those people who still want only hardcover books on their shelves.

Scribner's does a large mail-order business, "not to all, but to most of the U.N. countries," according to Kropotkin. Staff members of foreign consulates and delegations located nearby often come into the store and when they go abroad, they continue to be customers. Kropotkin likes to tell the story of one high-level foreign dignitary who came into the store surrounded by secret-service men; in one hour he bought $30,000 worth of books, paid in cash, and had them delivered to his private plane.

Scribner's will special order any book in print and the store issues a famous Christmas catalog every year.

Every fall, the store sponsors a book-fair program to a large number of schools in a fifty-mile radius of New York, such as New Canaan, Stamford, and Princeton. Working closely with parent-teacher associations, school officials, and librarians, the store sponsors a poster contest and organizes and holds a book fair. Some schools invite only students to the fairs. At others, the fair is sometimes a big event, lasting for two or three evenings, during which parents and friends also attend. The cosponsoring school or organization is given a percentage of whatever money is made from the sale of books, with the advice that that money be used to buy books to supplement their own library.

Kropotkin described the philosophy of the store: "To be as good as we possibly can be in our field; to provide a full range of books for the customer and a full range of collateral services. We know we're not perfect, and never will be—we don't know anyone who is—but we try our best!"

597 Fifth Avenue, New York, New York 10017; Tel. 212-486-4070.

Hours: Monday–Friday, 9:30 A.M.–7:00 P.M.; Saturday, 9:00 A.M.–5:00 P.M.

SAMUEL WEISER'S ORIENTAL AND OCCULT BOOKS

NEW YORK NEW YORK

Sam Weiser's is the largest occult and oriental bookstore in the country, if not the world, carrying over 200,000 used and out-of-print books and over 250,000 new books, all concerning almost every occult practice conceivable. Whether it is the kabbala, Zen Buddhism, yoga, the tarot, Hare Krishna, witch-craft, or numerology, Weiser's will probably have not just a shelf but often a whole section of books in the field, very neatly arranged and easy to find. The store attempts to carry *every* book or pamphlet that has been published on the specific occult discipline, and *if* a customer requests something that isn't in stock, the staff will order it.

Founded in 1926, with a small specialty in the occult, the store has mushroomed as interest in the occult has grown: from animal magnetism to spiritualism and parapsychology, which are all now passé, through the cult of hallucinogens in the 1960s to the consciousness expansion of TM today. Donald Weiser, Sam's son, now the store's owner, says the guiding philosophy of the store is to make the unknown known, without self-imposed censorship. Even though Weiser and his colleagues might disapprove of a particular occult ritual, they nevertheless carry any book about it.

Weiser's does a brisk mail-order business and will hold a request for an obscure book "until the store goes out of business." Recently the store was able to fill an order that had been on file since 1950. If the shop receives enough inquiries asking for an out-of-print book, it will occasionally buy the rights from the original publisher and issue the book in a new edition. The store has also been known to commission an author to do a book on an esoteric subject in which there is interest but about which no book exists. A catalog is issued once a year, and there is a free monthly newsletter.

A visit to Weiser's can be a memorable experience. The staff is highly schooled in the world of the occult and is very helpful to "beginners" of any particular practice, recommending the best books on the subject, sometimes giving explanatory mini-courses. Often customers can be seen meditating, standing on their heads in a corner, or instantly attempting a newly found Yogic posture in a book they have just discovered. Once a man went into *samadi*, becoming completely rigid, and had to be moved as though he were a human pole. The staff knew exactly how to handle him. He recovered an hour later and went back to browsing through the store.

740 Broadway (near 8th Street), New York, New York 10003; Tel. 212-777-6363. Hours: Monday–Friday, 9:30 A.M.–6:30 P.M.; Saturday, 9:30 A.M.–5:00 P.M.

BARNES AND NOBLE

NEW YORK
NEW YORK

According to the *Guinness Book of World Records*, Barnes and Noble is the "largest bookselling complex in the world." It also has to be one of the most unusual and exciting. Consider some of these facts: Rex Harrison once spent an entire afternoon browsing while a taxi waited outside with the meter running. A five-year-old emptied all the books out of a crate, crawled in, fell asleep, and was eventually discovered by a worried mother and a harried staff. A man called one day from Paris, ordered a book on economics, and then (rather un-economically) flew in the next day to pick it up. Every day for six months a man would come in at exactly 9:45 A.M. with a brown bag of coffee, sandwich, and dessert and spend the entire day reading law and engineering books. The Ellsberg defense attorneys bought books for background trial research. Authors often come in for remainders of their own books because they no longer have copies. The Citizens Exchange Corporation, a private cultural group in the Soviet Union, has a program allowing Soviet citizens to buy books from the store and have the bill sent to Russia. All purchases are approved with two exceptions: the citizens are not allowed to buy social science or history books. One man came in to study ways to bet at the races. A letter from a customer addressed to "The Largest Bookstore in the U.S." was promptly delivered. Students often spend entire days researching term papers.

The image of Barnes and Noble as a bookstore where things happen, however, is a relatively new one. For years, the store was thought of as mainly a supplier of textbooks, medical encyclopedias, and fairly esoteric tomes. In 1974, the store added a sales annex across the street from its main location on Fifth Avenue and Eighteenth Street and seemed to instantly revolutionize the retail book industry in New York City.

The sales annex is really the first book supermarket in the world. There are 2½ million books, all neatly arranged on easy-to-reach shelves located in wide, brightly lit aisles. Free lockers are provided so that shoppers can browse with ease. Shopping carts are provided for browsers, and for those who become a bit weary from walking up and down the miles of aisles, there are park benches spread about for resting. As an inducement to bring parents into the store, there are frequent puppet shows to occupy the children's attention while their parents search for their favorite books.

Most of the books for sale at the Barnes and Noble annex are remainders and publishers' overstocks, but there are also a large number of last year's textbooks and there are used-book sections, as well. Any book on the *New York Times*'s best-seller list is sold slightly above cost. In addition, some 250 other hardcover new books are sold well below list prices, and some 500 new paperbacks are also sold at substantial savings to customers. There is also a very large section, "Books for a Buck," where very attractive books can be bought for a dollar. In addition to the book bargains, there is a large classical record department.

Some four thousand customers come into Barnes and Noble on an average day; twice that number shop there on busy days. Although there are few other retail businesses in that part of Manhattan, it is now becoming quite difficult to find a parking space (at one time it was the easiest place in the city) because of the huge numbers of book-buyers who descend upon Barnes and Noble every day.

A small version of the annex has recently opened at Rockefeller Center in New York and is proving to be even busier than the store downtown, and a Boston store, also just opened, is also doing well. Both are patterned after the larger annex and have its many features, such as the special sales tables, the shopping carts, the lockers, and the discounts on best sellers. There are also twenty other smaller stores spread around the country, mostly on or near college campuses.

Most customers find it virtually impossible to go into a Barnes and Noble store and exit without finding at least *one* book that is of interest. Morris Wogman, vice-president of marketing of the store, puts it this way: "Most book-buyers are not looking for scholarly and intellectual titles; they want books that entertain, or help them improve lives or life-styles. They are average people like you and I. Barnes and Noble gives them what they want."

105 Fifth Avenue, New York, New York 10003; Tel. 212-255-8100. Hours: Monday–Friday, 9:45 A.M.–6:45 P.M.; Saturday, 9:45 A.M.– 6:00 P.M.
Sale Annex, 126 Fifth Avenue, New York, New York 10011; Tel. 212-255-8100. Hours: Monday–Friday, 9:45 A.M.–6:45 P.M.; Satur-

day, 9:45 A.M.–6:00 P.M.; Sunday, 10:00 A.M.-5:00 P.M.
Sale Annex, 600 Fifth Avenue, New York, New York 10020; Tel.
212-765-0590. Hours: Monday–Friday, 9:45 A.M.–6:45 P.M.; Saturday, 9:45 A.M.–6:00 P.M.; Sunday, 11:00 A.M.–5:00 P.M.

Give me a condor's quill!
Give me Vesuvius' crater for an inkstand! . . .
To produce a mighty book, you must choose a mighty theme.
                                        HERMAN MELVILLE

THE BALLET SHOP   NEW YORK
                                        NEW YORK

There is a special magic about the Ballet Shop, a small but
vital bookstore located within pirouetting distance of New
York's Lincoln Center. Perhaps it's the fact that almost every
inch of the shop is used for prints, oil paintings, lithographs,
books, and other memorabilia concerning the ballet—and all
for sale—making it look a little like the backstage dressing room
of Isadora Duncan. Or else it might be the clientele: nicely
dressed people who often stop in on matinee days of the New
York City Ballet (conveniently located around the corner from
the shop) to buy copies of the biography of Nijinsky or an
autographed photograph of Baryshnikov; dancers, young,
flushed, still with leotards under their clothes, picking up a
copy of Edwin Denby's *Looking at the Dance* because it was
mentioned in class an hour ago.

Here it is possible to buy a button with a picture of Rudolf
Nureyev on it; autographed toe shoes of famous ballerinas;
rare, original photographs of well-known dancers; classic programs, paintings, statues, and some four thousand books on all
forms of dance, ballet, opera, and mime.

The shop is owned and mainly operated by Norman Crider,
who began collecting ballet memorabilia over twenty-five

years ago. As world juggling champion, he lived all over the world, and while in Paris he stayed in the home of a dancer and became fascinated with the ballet. Now dance enthusiasts benefit from Crider's knowledege of the literature and can buy new and used paperbound and hardcover books, everything from a biography of Margot Fonteyn to Alfred Knopf's magnificent new volume on the New York City Ballet.

The Ballet Shop issues a catalog of its books and other memorabilia and accepts Visa and American Express credit cards.

Crider cites three books as his most popular: *Days with Ulanova, The Art of Margot Fonteyn*, and a book on Balanchine by Bernard Taper. "I could sell *thousands* of these but they are now out of print. Publishers should reprint their most popular titles," he says. He explains the popularity of some of the books he sells: "Ballets are now mobbed and there has been an explosion of interest in all kinds of dance, touched off by the skyrocketing popularity of Rudolf Nureyev."

1887 Broadway, New York, New York 10023; Tel. 212-581-7990. Hours: Monday–Friday, 11:00 A.M.–8:00 P.M.; Saturday, 10:00 A.M.–8:00 P.M.

WEYHE ART BOOKS, INC.
NEW YORK NEW YORK

Deborah Dennis took over this bookstore when the founder—her grandfather—died in 1971. Weyhe actually began in the book business on Charing Cross Road, in England, and started his U.S. career in 1918 with a few books in the back of a plumbing store. By 1924, he had taken over the entire building, and according to Ms. Dennis, it's been that way ever since, with books piled every which way, in three rooms.

Deborah worked summers in the bookstore and at night

while in school. Her grandfather had a heart attack and had to "rule from upstairs" while she took over the actual running of the shop. At his death, Deborah took over the operation on a full-time basis.

"We don't appeal to the carriage trade," explains Ms. Dennis. "We've never been particularly aggressive, and people come to us because others don't have the stock. Many customers are art lovers, seeking a particular print." Deborah's philosophy is to run the gamut, have on hand as much as she can afford. "I'm still close enough to my student days, so I also carry the small discount books and remainders," she adds.

The shop has a nostalgic, nineteenth-century, Dickensian atmosphere. And its proprietress has been referred to as "the Billie Jean King" of the art book field. She is one of the three leading women booksellers in this field, the others being in Florence and Paris. She does, indeed, play an excellent game of tennis, and closes the shop for a month each year to go to Nova Scotia, play tennis, garden, and relax.

In addition to the three floors of the store, there are huge warehouses and an upstairs gallery of original graphics. The shop held the first major exhibition of Günter Grass's lithographs, for example.

Deborah is in the business for the fun of it. She likes to hunt out a requested book and once took four years to track one down and deliver it. "Often," she says, "we'll tell a customer there's no such book, and then find it the very next day. We've even hunted down artists we've never heard of—say a sixteenth-century Genoese."

"We don't make a profit," she claims, "but we're personally honorable. I'd like it if the books weren't three deep, but, personally, I wouldn't change it."

Neither would we.

794 Lexington Avenue, New York, New York 10021; Tel. 212-TE8-5466. Hours: Monday–Saturday, 9:30 A.M.–5:30 P.M.

LIGHTHOUSE
BOOKSTORE

RYE
NEW YORK

Founded in 1946 by Goddard Light, the Lighthouse Bookstore in Rye, New York is now owned and operated by Richard T. Stearns, who acquired the operation in 1975. There are seven full-time employees, and the shop keeps approximately eighteen thousand books in stock, covering some ten thousand titles. While the stock is general, specialization is in the areas of cookbooks and science fiction. The store sells books both new and used, both hardbound and paperback, and both fiction and nonfiction. Clients at this shop are offered an assortment of special services, including special orders for any book in print and search services for out-of-print books. There are semiannual sales, and the store also offers free gift-wrapping. Mailing service is available, and the shop also has a rental library.

Anybody can be placed on the mailing list just by asking, and there is no charge. As mailing service is also available, this could prove very worthwhile to any bibliophile. The store already has happy and satisfied customers in such far-flung places as Brazil, France, Saudi Arabia, and the Philippines. The typical walk-in customer is an affluent suburbanite, and often a publishing company executive, as many live nearby. The well-stocked shelves are complemented by the friendly, efficient, and helpful staff. The shop is attractive and spacious, with more than ample browsing space. About one-quarter of its space is located at street level, with the balance of the shop located downstairs along with the offices and storage space.

In addition to the books, Lighthouse also sells cards, imprinted and boxed stationery, maps, bookplates, and bookends. The shop only accepts house charges, but will also accept your personal check with proper identification.

The Lighthouse Bookstore is located on a main shopping

street in a residential New York suburb with ample and free off-street parking facilities.

The spirit of this shop is nicely summed up by its owner, who says, "We'd like every customer to leave with a book in his hand and a smile on his face."

20 Purchase Street, Rye, New York 10580; Tel. 914-967-0966. Hours: Monday–Saturday, 9:00 A.M.–5:30 P.M.

Who gives a good book gives more than cloth, paper and ink . . . more than leather, parchment and words. He reveals a foreword of his thoughts, a dedication of his friendship, a page of his presence, a chapter of himself, and an index of his love.

WILLIAM A. WARD

North Carolina

To: The Muses
From: Michelle Queen

My name is Michelle Queen. I love your store's wide selection of books. I have bought many books from your store, and here is a list of a few of them:

1. The Hobbit (1 set)
2. Rabbit Hill
3. Nancy Drew Books
4. All Creatures Great and Small
5. All Things Bright and Beautiful
6. Marguerite Henry's Horse Books
7. Moshie Cat
8. Just a Dog
9. The Rescuers
10. Police Dog

I plan to buy the book *All Things Wise and Wonderful* when it comes out in early August.

I really appreciate all the kindness and attention you have shown me in your store.

Respectfully,
Michelle Queen, 5th grade
Drexel, N.C.

The above letter is an excellent indication of what the Muses is all about: a store that stocks a great variety of books and will take the time to work with children—and adults—in the selection of books that they need and want. The Muses is quite simply one of the finest bookstores in the United States.

Marion H. Lieberman, who has chronicled the store in news-

173

paper and magazine articles and also edits the store's own fascinating cultural publication, *Onstage*, contributes this description:

Most people call it a bookstore—but The Muses is actually a cultural center, focusing on the deepest interests and creative needs of people of all ages. Within the cream-color, star-shaped building designed like a temple to the nine ancient Greek goddesses are books and art encompassing all the subjects the Muses represent: drama, science, comedy, history, religion, poetry, music, romance, and heroic action.

At The Muses, the "in" place to be, it is not unusual to make new friends, participate in impromptu, stimulating discussions about everything and anything under the sun, solve problems, discuss marriage plans. On special evenings, there are "culture raps"—lectures and programs presented informally, with listeners sitting in a semicircle on the gold shag carpet to hear highly qualified speakers in varied fields.

There are mind exercisers like puzzles—crossword, jigsaw and round—The Shakespeare Game, Executive Decision, and an art auction game; hobby materials, crafts aids, classical records; coloring books and graphics, posters and astrological charts; unique gifts.

For the little ones, there are toys, novelties, stuffed animals—and even a brown bear rug to snuggle into while Momma is browsing. Within The Muses are the pathways to adventure, excitement, new experiences, broadened horizons, ideas, education—and fun.

Founded by Shirley and Frank Sprinkle in 1972, after they had left the precarious oil business ("We spent all of our spare time in bookstores," says Shirley), the Muses is housed in a star-shaped building designed specifically for book browsers: glass and sunlight are everywhere; a dome at the top allows a direct view of the sky; the walls are hung with depictions of the nine muses; outside, there is a Japanese garden, a small, bubbling pool, bamboo poles and ginkgo trees, giving the entire area the look and feeling of a garden in Kyoto.

Inside, there are over 30,000 titles, consisting of all new paperbound and hardbound, fiction and nonfiction books. The store specializes in books on North Carolina and in educational aids for teachers and students.

Even though the Muses is in a small rural town of a population

174

of sixteen thousand, it draws readers and browsers from all over the state—including nearby resident, former senator Sam Ervin—because of the excellence of its stock and its varied services. The store will special order books, gift-wrap any purchase free of charge, mail to any destination in the world.

Shirley Sprinkle describes her philosophy as bookseller: "My goal is to get the right book and customer together, to advise *when asked*, to provide material for the dispensation of knowledge, to aid in the improving the educational level of the community, and to create an atmosphere where our customers can enjoy exchanging ideas with one another." The Muses succeeds as few stores do.

P.O. Box 1268 (West Union Cross Roads), Morganton, North Carolina 28655; Tel. 704-433-1314. Hours: seven days a week, 364 days a year, closed Christmas only, Monday–Saturday, 9:00 A.M.– 9:00 P.M.; Sunday, 1:00 P.M.–7:00 P.M.

What a convenient and delightful world is this world of books! If you bring to it not the obligations of the student, or look upon it as the opiate for idleness, but enter it rather with the enthusiasm of the adventurer!
DAVID GRAYSON

Ohio

WYOMING BOOK SHOP   **CINCINNATI
                                          OHIO**

Tea on Saturday afternoon, in company with a visiting author, is one of the attractions of the Wyoming Book Shop. The shop was founded in 1969 by Joan Schneider and was purchased in 1973 by Ann Bernstein, its present owner. It has seven employees.

The store sells both paper and hardbound books, new books only. It specializes in new fiction and nonfiction, as well as juvenile books. It's a neighborhood store, one that expands into the surrounding community, serving as a reflection of that community. It's an area of readers and writers, one that has produced some famous and important names—as Nikki Giovanni and Thomas Berger, among others.

Mailings, which are limited to previous customers, consist of such items as the Scribner's catalog. In addition to books, the store also sells bookplates, bookmarks, and T-shirts, and Master Charge and Visa charge cards are accepted. The shop handles gift registrations and special orders.

8418 Vine Street, Cincinnati, Ohio 45216; Tel. 513-761-6248. Hours: Monday–Saturday, 10:00 A.M.–5:00 P.M.

COVENTRY BOOKS   **CLEVELAND HEIGHTS
                       OHIO**

Ellen Strong, who now owns the Coventry Books store, emphasizes that this shop serves as a community information center for the neighborhood. But while she used to have poetry

176

readings, space got tight, and the room formerly used for the readings is now used for books.

The shop does search for books, but in a passive way, keeping lists of customer wants and then, when a book does come in, trying to match the customer with the book. Similarly, a mailing list, once kept active, proved to be too time-consuming and was dropped.

The shop was founded by Brett Anderson, Linn S. Hopkins, and Ms. Strong in 1972. It now has ten employees and stocks some 100,000 books in all general categories, including fiction and nonfiction, hardback and softbound, both new and used. Specialties here include fiction, science fiction, and occult and feminist literature. The shop consists of some five thousand square feet, with books in like areas of interest grouped together. In addition to books, the shop also sells calendars, posters, and some magazines not carried by local distributors. It accepts Master Charge and Visa credit cards.

Ms. Strong describes the ambience as friendly, congenial, and "esoterically funny at times." The staff will offer help if you need it, and leave you alone if you do not.

Ms. Strong explains that the closer management is to the customer, the better the bookstore will be—personal relationships are important in a personal bookstore.

Coventry Books has been both immortalized in an underground comic and lauded by the *Cleveland Plain Dealer* as one of the top bookstores in the state of Ohio.

1824 Coventry Road, Cleveland Heights, Ohio 44118; Tel. 216-932-8111. Hours: Monday–Friday, 10:00 A.M.–10:00 P.M.; Saturday, 10:00 A.M.–7:00 P.M.; Sunday, 12:00 Noon–6:00 P.M.

When I get a little money, I buy books; and if any is left, I buy food and clothes.

ERASMUS

177

THE FLORENCE O. WILSON BOOKSTORE
WOOSTER OHIO

Forty-five thousand books, consisting of over five thousand text titles, fifteen thousand paper and four thousand cloth, are looked after by ten employees at this shop, founded by the College of Wooster in 1866. The shop sells paper and hardbound books, fiction and nonfiction, new and used. Of course, a great deal of the stock caters to the college trade, but the store also sells general, paperback, children's, and used books—which means that it also buys used books.

Special services include the offer to obtain any book published anywhere in the world. Events held regularly include author's parties, lectures, and guest speakers. Mail-order requests are serviced also, and the store's operators aver that "the best people in the world browse here." The store accepts Visa and Master Charge, and its philosophy, simply stated, is "to sell any book one may wish."

The store is owned by Don Noll.

The College of Wooster, Wooster, Ohio 44691; Tel. 216-264-9643. Hours: Monday–Friday, 9:00 A.M.–4:00 P.M.; Saturday, 9:00 A.M.–1:00 P.M.

To buy books only because they were published by an eminent printer, is much as if a man should buy clothes that did not fit him, only because made by some famous tailor.

ALEXANDER POPE

Pennsylvania

HOW-TO-DO-IT BOOK SHOP

PHILADELPHIA
PENNSYLVANIA

Want to know how to find happiness? Would you like to know how to make money at the races? Maybe you'd like to start your own corporation for under fifty dollars, or learn how to parachute, be a secretary, analyze handwriting, publish your own book, make your own picture frames, or enjoy sexual relations with much more zest. You can learn to do these and thousands of other things—almost anything that might come to mind—by paying a visit to the How-To-Do-It Book Shop. The store has twenty thousand titles that instruct, guide, teach, aid, tutor, coach, and train. Located on a small street in downtown Philadelphia, the How-To-Do-It must rank as one of the most unusual bookstores in the United States: here you will find no fiction, biography, or history. It is impossible to find a copy of *Roots*, *Jaws*, *Passages*, or any other best seller, as a matter of fact, unless it falls under the aegis of being a "how-to" book. The *only* books that the store carries are "how-to" books and they are totally universal in that area.

Browse in the store long enough and you'll see some unusual happenings: a doctor looking for a book on bookbinding; a young teenager wanting to buy a book on how to make a million; a mild-mannered, almost milquetoast type glancing through a book on how to debate effectively or how to master the art of Kung Fu.

It's easy to browse through the store. The owners, Elizabeth and Herbert Shugar, are strict, however, about people taking notes, boning up on their favorite subject and then not buying a book: "I can't afford to run a reference library for the conve-

179

nience of noncustomers," Herb states gently. What the Shugars *will* do, however, is give advice as to what is the best book on a particular subject for a specific customer—a book to suit his needs. If they can't match up an exact book with a specific subject, they will come as close as they can. One customer, a horse breeder, was desperate to learn how to shoe a horse. Such books are hard to find but the shop searched them out and eventually produced three titles on the subject.

"We do get to know what's on people's minds," says Herb. "There is a great deal of interest in buying real estate and buying country property. Auto repair is increasingly important because of the high cost of getting it done. Everyone is economy minded. That's the real reason for the success of the store."

The most popular book sold at the How-To-Do-It is *How To Keep Your Volkswagen Alive*, by John Muir, bought by VW owners, who have traditionally been interested in economy. But people who drive a Mercedes also want auto repair books. They might not do the repairs themselves, but they want to know what the mechanic is doing. Unfortunately, the How-To-Do-It does not issue a catalog, but the staff will fill mail orders for any book in stock. The store accepts Master Charge.

Architects and engineers often come to the store to buy technical books concerning their field. Marketing people are interested in books on advertising, layout, and graphic arts. The store also sells many books about old-fashioned crafts, such as bread-making and carpentry. There is also an enormous section of cookbooks of all types of food.

What is the most unusual request the How-To-Do-It has had for a book? There was the man who wanted a book on how to raise cattle. And then someone once wanted a book on how to shrink heads, not how to psychoanalyze, but how to actually shrink human heads. "We couldn't supply the book," says Herb, "but I'm sure it exists. By now, I believe that a book exists on how to do absolutely anything."

1608 Sansom Street, Philadelphia, Pennsylvania 19103; Tel. 215-563-1516. Hours: Monday–Friday, 10:00 A.M.–6:00 P.M.; Saturday, 10:30 A.M.–5:00 P.M.

MIDDLE EARTH BOOKS   PHILADELPHIA
                                     PENNSYLVANIA

This is a nicely cluttered, relaxed bookstore that specializes in poetry, art, and the humanities. The clientele consists mainly of students, both in and out of school. "We're one of the last outposts, unfortunately, of primary concern for quality of books over economic concerns," states one of the salespeople. "An island of sanity in a world of pain." Although they carry only new books, they do have a section of out-of-print small press literature. In addition to books, Middle Earth also stocks some note cards, calendars and maps.

Perhaps one of the most interesting aspects of Middle Earth is its constant and sensitive attempt to stock books that will affect people's lives. The store's personnel also love books in a way that is both charming and mystical. "When the store is closed, the books are asleep," one of them told us.

1134 Pine Street, Philadelphia, Pennsylvania 19107; Tel. 215-WA2-6824. Hours: Monday–Saturday, 12:00 Noon–6:00 P.M. and 8:00 P.M.–Midnight.

People say that life is the thing, but I prefer reading.
                                     LOGAN PEARSALL SMITH

181

THE FIRST EDITION BOOKSTORE

STATE COLLEGE AND HARRISBURG PENNSYLVANIA

The initial reaction most people have to the First Edition Bookstore in the State College, Pennsylvania, mall (and to its sister branch in the Harrisburg East Mall in Harrisburg) is total surprise at the enormous number of books each carries— over 150,000 books between them. The shelves fairly soar against the walls, artfully and efficiently crammed with tomes; the top compartments are only reachable by various wooden library ladders spread attractively throughout the store. Somehow it is easy to forget one is in a store located inside a mall. Adventurous browsers can search for books atop the ladders, or acrobatic clerks are only too willing to make the ascent for any customer who wishes to remain earthbound. In addition to the thousands of shelved books, there are rows and bins and tables and displays of books spread throughout the store, containing books that range from the current best seller to a huge selection of bargain books. The First Edition's main stock in books, however, is new hardcover and paperback books (mass-market and high quality trade paperbacks), with excellent sections in photography and cooking, where it is possible to buy a collection of Matthew Brady photographs or a recipe book of unusual brunches.

One of the ways that owner Arnie Rubin keeps his stores so well stocked is through the use of his private pilot's license. If a distributor is slow in getting a shipment of books to the First Edition, Rubin, assisted by his wife, Arlene, will fly anywhere on the East Coast to retrieve his order, sometimes saving weeks in getting new books into his stores. He also flies to New York every few weeks to visit publishers and other bookstores, distributors and remainder houses to make certain that the First Edition will, indeed, be first in getting shipments of books that are in demand by his customers and to purchase bargain and sale books that will be of interest.

The First Edition remains open late (both stores until 9:30) and takes Visa and Master Charge. Mail-order customers can be included on the mailing list by visiting or writing to the store and simply giving their names and addresses.

Rubin attempts to do everything he can to keep all those connected with the store happy, and that includes, he says, "not only the customers but my supplier and my own employees, as well." The result is a pleasant, totally efficient store that is a literate addition to the community it serves.

Nittany Mall, State College, Pennsylvania 16801; Tel. 814-238-5724. Hours: Monday–Saturday, 10:00 A.M.–9:30 P.M.
Harrisburg East Mall, Harrisburg, Pennsylvania 17111; Tel. 717-861-1015. Hours: Monday–Saturday, 10:00 A.M.–9:30 P.M.

Specifically it may appear that I am more interested in books than in people; but I think it is nearer the mark to say that I am more interested in people as they are revealed to me in books than as they reveal themselves to me in daily contact.

VINCENT STARRET

183

Tennessee

HERMITAGE BOOKSTORE, INC.

The Hermitage Bookstore is a small but well-stocked store which refuses to carry only current best sellers. Thus, the shop maintains a strong backlist in poetry, psychology, business, art, and other areas, and this fact alone makes it unique in this area of the country.

Most of the Hermitage's customers are college students and "book people," people who seek the store out to find specific titles, to browse among the good books, or to talk "book talk." Owners Jane and Jonas Kisber encourage this: Jane says that "books are an important part, not only of our culture, but of our civilization. Reading needs to be encouraged as a pleasure and not as a chore. Conversation is an art, and a bookstore is a conducive environment for conversation, ideas, and friendship."

Travelers are welcomed, too. The Hermitage provides free maps of Jackson and any directions needed to find your way around the area. The shop is conveniently located near both the Holiday Inn and the Ramada Inn.

Children are encouraged to visit this store, which has thoughtfully provided a private alcove with a small table and chairs where the youngsters can browse through children's books. For the taller folk, one side of the paneled room holds a "conversation corner," with couch, chairs, and a coffee table.

Hermitage Bookstore sells some cards and posters and selected games, as well as books. The store will special order books for a customer at no extra charge, and provides free gift-wrapping for all purchases as well as free delivery within

184

the Jackson area. There is a Christmas catalog, and interested customers can be placed on the mailing list simply by requesting it.

The shop holds autograph sessions and "local author days," featuring such writers as Jesse Hill Ford and William Haas, and there are occasional poetry readings. Hermitage Bookstore also keeps careful track of school reading lists and makes sure to have all required books on hand; books are delivered free to schools.

The shop is a warm, friendly place, where you can find good books and nice people.

Hamilton Hills Shopping Center, Jackson, Tennessee 38301; Tel. 901-668-1407. Hours: Monday–Saturday, 10:00 A.M.–5:00 P.M.

There are some knightly souls who even go so far as to make their visits to bookshops a kind of chivalrous errantry at large. They go in not because they need any certain volume, but because they feel there may be some book that needs them.
CHRISTOPHER MORLEY

Texas

TAYLORS, INC.

DALLAS
TEXAS

We'd thought those tall stories about Texas were only rumors. Surely the largest (contiguous) state didn't necessarily grow the tallest people, or the beefiest steers, or the deepest oil wells, or the biggest *everything*.

But it does have one of the biggest bookstores! Taylors has been ranked among the five largest independently owned bookstores in the United States. As of this writing, Taylors has more than a quarter of a million books in stock, covering over 200 subject classifications. But considering the store's normal rate of growth, these numbers will probably be considerably higher by the time you read this.

Taylors began in 1969 as Preston Books, a small bookstore in the Preston Center West shopping center, opened under the sole management and operation of Martha Taylor. The original twelve-hundred-square-foot store grew rapidly to its current nine thousand square feet, and in the process became a family-owned corporation, with Henry E. Taylor as its president.

In 1976, Taylors moved into its current, brand-new quarters in Preston Center East shopping center. The giant store leases its own building, with a modern, multi-windowed exterior and an incredibly well-organized interior. To prevent customers from getting lost among the bookshelves and never being heard from again, Taylors provides what the staff refer to as their "road maps"—a complimentary store directory, which helps customers locate categories and customer service departments throughout the store. Twenty-eight employees are also on hand to offer specific assistance.

Taylors sells new books in both paperback and hardback, fiction and nonfiction. There is a special section for current best sellers, as well as books on virtually any subject you might want. Some of the categories are fairly traditional: literature, cooking, plays, poetry. But Taylors stocks books in some rather esoteric areas, as well. Astrology and meditation, of course, but how about numerology, and pyramidology, and even Ufology? And a large section called Texana, in honor of the home state.

Here are a few more: travel, music, treasure hunting, wines and spirits, American Indian, sports, nutrition, Gothics, child care, Oriental arts and antiques, automotive repair, atlases, boating, children's books, and women's studies. In short, if you want a book that's currently in print, or if you want to see what books are available in a certain subject area, Taylors probably has what you're looking for.

The store has a mailing list for customers and services mail-order requests. Master Charge and Visa credit cards are accepted.

When we studied the history of the store's phenomenal growth in less than a decade, it seemed evident that Taylors must be doing something exceedingly right, so we asked its president, Henry E. Taylor (husband of the store's founder, who now serves as its secretary-treasurer) for the Taylors' philosophy as booksellers. His answer: "Books are a consumable product. The 'reader' is, in reality, a consumer. Therefore, the largest number of books covering the widest range of subjects should be aimed at this consumer-market, supported by good service, capable personnel, an efficient operation, and, above all, management administrative expertise." Taylors seems determined to live up to these goals.

4001 Northwest Parkway, Dallas, Texas 75225; Tel. 214-363-1500. Hours: Monday–Saturday, 9:30 A.M.–6:00 P.M.; Thursday till 9:00 P.M.

"It's a new book," insisted the annoyed customer. "I think it's on the best-seller list. You must at least have heard of it! It's called *Crisises*, and I'm very anxious to get a copy. If you don't have it in stock now, can't you at least order it for me?"

The clerk thought a moment. "Yes, sir, if we don't have the book we'll certainly order it for you. But if you'll follow me for a moment, there is a book right over here that you may find interesting. It's by Gail Sheehy, and it's called *Passages*. Do you suppose this could be what you're looking for."

"Uh. *Passages*. I could have sworn . . ."

"Well, it's a natural mistake. The book does deal with 'the Predictable Crises of Adult Life,' as it says on the cover."

"Yes. Well, thank you. I guess this is the one."

Books Inc. is used to such mistakes. The five employees take it all in stride, and calmly assist their customers in locating the books of their choice.

Books Inc. is a general bookstore, which sells mostly new, hardbound books, in both fiction and non-fiction. But out of its roughly 50,000 titles, it does have a few special collections. There are substantial numbers of cookbooks and art books, as well as books on gardening and on "Texana," and it carries a large number of children's books.

The store also carries imported gift items, artwork, posters, and cards. It provides free gift wrapping and will mail your purchases at your instruction. You may charge items with Master Charge or Visa.

While Books Inc. does not have a catalog, it will service mail order requests and will special-order any book that is in print.

Located in one of Houston's famous shopping-centers-for-the-affluent, surrounded by expensive, chic stores, Books Inc. is often visited by "the famous, the rich, the wishers," according to owner H.P. Albrecht. The store holds selective autograph parties, and tries to keep a wide range of books in stock, an "intellectual something" for everyone.

But sometimes, that something is a little hard to determine. Like the time a customer wanting a copy of Colleen McCullough's *The Thorn Birds*, asked instead for *Thorn Bees*. Or the self-help devotee who wanted to buy a copy of *Your Erroneous Zones* and asked the clerk to give him *Your Erroneous Sounds*. Maybe he'd heard about it on the radio.

Books Inc., 2620 Westheimer, Houston, Texas 77098; Tel. 713-529-4238; Hours: Monday–Friday, 9:30 A.M.–6:00 P.M.; Saturday, 9:00 A.M.–5:30 P.M.

Where is human nature so weak as in the bookstore?
                        HENRY WARD BEECHER

BROWN BOOK SHOP, INC.   HOUSTON TEXAS

"Thoroughness and attention to detail," excellent recommendations to anybody in any area, are what the people at Brown's feel to be their personal philosophy of bookselling. The store, located in the heart of downtown Houston, boasts a thorough inventory and knowledgeable personnel to man the shop. The store was founded by Ted V. Brown, in 1946, and has been doing a thriving business ever since (Houston is one of the most active "book cities" in the U.S.). It now has seventeen employees and about 100,000 books in stock. The store sells new books only, paper and hardbound, fiction and nonfiction, with special emphasis on scientific/technical books as well as art books. This is one of the few stores in the U.S. that carries all of Samuel Eliot Morrison's fifteen-volume *History of U.S. Naval Operations in World War II.*

The store also does a large mail-order business, shipping books to all the continents, and services include searching for out-of-print books. The store has a mailing list to support their mail-order activities, and you can apply to be on this list at no charge.

The clientele is mature, aged twenty-five and up, with interests in all the sciences save medicine and law. This, according to the owner, is acknowledged to be the best bookstore in the Southwest and one of the best bookstores in America.

The store sells books only and will accept Master Charge and Visa credit cards. It has been well reviewed in several publications, including the *Saturday Review of Literature*.

1219 Fanin Street, Houston, Texas 77002; Tel. 713-652-3937. Hours: Monday–Thursday, 8:00 A.M.–8:00 P.M.; Friday, 8:00 A.M.–6:00 P.M.; Saturday, 8:00 A.M.–5:00 P.M.

All that mankind has done, thought, gained or been,
it is lying as in magic preservation in the pages of books.
They are the choicest possessions of men.
                                                    THOMAS CARLYLE

Utah

SAM WELLER'S ZION BOOK STORE

In 1924 a Mormon convert, like the pioneers who came in the nineteenth century, came to Salt Lake City from Germany and, five years later, opened the Zion Book Store. Sam Weller operated the shop until 1946, when his son Sam took over. A scant year and a half later, the store was struck by a devastating fire that ruined the stock and put the firm out of business for months.

You can't hold a good shop down, however, and now there are over ten thousand square feet of selling floor and a mezzanine of twenty-five thousand new and used books. The store does an annual volume of better than $750,000. Books are sold exclusively.

When a book of strong local interest—such as on Mormonism or Utah—is published, Weller promotes it and does a land-office business as a result. He sold hundreds of copies of *The Uneasy Chair*, a biography of a Utah author, Bernard De Voto, written by another Utah writer, Wallace Stegner. He really services his clientele, offering to search for out-of-print books, and goes out of his way to please. He delights in finding a book that a customer is looking for and achieves a great deal of satisfaction in matching the customer to the book. Conversely, he finds it terribly frustrating when a client requests a book that he cannot locate because it may have gone out of print, or when a publisher's shipping delays result in cancellations.

Weller has a complete general stock of titles, but also specializes in western Americana and books about the Mormons. He does a massive mail-order business that results from

191

his catalog, which brings orders from the world over. Many universities are aware of the Mormon area of specialization at this bookshop, and he does a thriving business with the schools.

Weller maintains that when publishers are planning a new list, they will consult with the editors, the salesmen, and their own instincts, but they would do a great deal better, he feels, to consult with the booksellers on the front lines. It is the man who will ultimately push the book over the counter who has the best instincts as to what the public will buy.

The shop does stock rare books, and these are kept in a walk-in book vault, where almost anything in rare and out-of-print books can be found.

Weller complains, too, about the fact that he's always some two thousand miles from the publishers, for this often results in a breakdown in communication. Still, this problem does not seem to inhibit the growth and prosperity of this fine operation.

254 South Main Street, Salt Lake City, Utah 84101; Tel. 801-328-2586. Hours: Monday and Friday, 9:30 A.M.–9:00 P.M.; Tuesday, Wednesday, Thursday, and Saturday, 9:30 A.M.–6:00 P.M.

Vermont

THE BOOK CELLAR

Russell M. Stockman, who owns and operates the Book Cellar, is one of the more independent and outspoken booksellers in the country. This is how he describes his store: "First a word about style. We are not merchandisers, but booksellers. We know books, value them, *read* them, and delight in getting good ones into the hands of others who feel the same way. We cannot begin to compete with the high-volume, discount stores in the cities—except in terms of personal service. We recognize that people need a reliable source for all kinds of books beyond the few dozen best sellers of the moment, and that fewer and fewer shops these days have the knowledge or willingness to be of help. Lastly, we don't like computers much. The publishing business employs a lot of them these days, and each day's mail brings us fresh batches of their mistakes. We prefer our own, human mistakes. None of the great old bookshops that inspired the likes of Christopher Morley or Helene Hanff had computers—or inventory control. And it was reading books like theirs that led us into the business in the first place. Why have a bookshop if you can't be fussily eccentric about it? Our inventory often gets out of 'control' because we forget things. Yet that frees space on the shelves for things no profit-conscious computer would dream of ordering, and that makes for livelier browsing."

Despite the statement above, the Book Cellar *does* in fact keep up with best sellers; it also maintains a remarkable number of titles from publishers' backlists—both hardcover and paperback—and the store's range is eclectic. Here is a random

193

sampling: fiction, criticism, poetry, art and photography, music, reference, biography, cookery, natural history, gardening, psychology, travel, theology, children's books, philosophy, anthropology, and a huge section on Vermontiana and New England, both new and used.

The Book Cellar will order any book for a customer, gift-wrap the book, and mail it anywhere in the world. There is also an unusual out-of-print search service. Stockman explains that service, thusly: "We do not maintain a general stock of used books, though we do buy and sell antiquarian books relating to Vermont, and we distribute at odd intervals a listing of our current holdings in this field. Through the professional weekly we are nonetheless in touch with used-book dealers around the country, and we regularly advertise for used and rare titles of all kinds. No such search service can guarantee results, of course, but in many instances this can be an efficient source for a copy of that wonderful old children's book that the dog ate, or a set of Dickens like the one grandpa had. In every case the customer is told the price of such a find before it is bought, and may take it or turn it down with no charge . . . and no hard feelings."

Stockman's philosophy of bookselling is that it is more rewarding to eke out a living getting distinguished books into the hands of discerning buyers than to get rich pushing the same books or "products" that fill the shelves of every other bookshop. Is the Book Cellar a "great" bookstore? Stockman is refreshingly candid when he says that it may not be, but he adds that "we are only notable for uncompromising independence, personal service, and our knowledge of good books." What more can a bookstore give?

120 Main Street, Brattleboro, Vermont 05301; Tel. 802-254-6026. Hours: Monday–Saturday, 9:00 A.M.–5:30 P.M.; Friday, 9:00 A.M.– 9:00 P.M.

BOOK STACKS, INC.

The building that houses this bookstore was, in the late 1800s, a brick boilerhouse which provided the steam power for a nearby factory complex which manufactured patent medicines. Today, the brick walls remain, and some of the old niches where the boilers were have been converted into alcoves for fiction and children's books. The nineteenth-century feeling still abounds in the store, and with its many chairs and couches, it is an ideal place to browse. The store also shares space with a used bookstore, the Frayed Page, which is on the back balcony.

Book Stacks is a cooperative venture owned by four young book-lovers who also work in the store, all duties and decisions being made coequally and by consensus.

The store has an extensive stock in many sections: fiction, poetry, building, feminism, gay rights, political theory, photography, and juvenile. They will order any book from any publisher, search for out-of-print titles, have regular sectional sales, and provide books for prisoners at cost. The owners conduct a number of parties on a regular basis, including autographings and openings for local craftspeople who display their wares.

Book Stacks is a store that is a pleasant place to look for books. The owners/managers obviously put a strong emphasis on environment. They enjoy their work and they enjoy selling books.

118 Pine Street, Burlington, Vermont 05401; Tel. 802-862-8513. Hours: Monday–Thursday, 9:30 A.M.–8:00 P.M.; Friday, 9:30 A.M.– 9:00 P.M.; Saturday, 9:30 A.M.–6:00 P.M.

THE VERMONT
BOOK SHOP

MIDDLEBURY
VERMONT

Someday you may be curious as to how and why Lord Byron's sword came to be permanently housed in the Montpelier, Vermont, museum. Or you might care to know more details of how a crowd of fifteen thousand once congregated in the Stratton Mountains (also in Vermont) to hear Daniel Webster give one of his memorable speeches. Or you could be seeking information about what role the citizens of Vermont played in the War of 1812. If the history, people, culture, or lore of one of America's most beautiful states interests you, chances are the Vermont Book Shop will have a book on its shelves that contains the information you seek.

Aside from its substantial collection of books on Vermontiana, the Vermont Book Shop is one of the best-stocked bookstores of hardback books of all kinds in northern New England. Owner Robert Dike Blair, a pipe-smoking professorial type who is quick to correct his customers' grammar, has been running the shop for over twenty-five years and explains why people come from as far off as fifty miles to buy books in his shop: "We try to get the right book together with the right person and we stock books—from paperbacks to lavish art books—that other stores simply don't carry." Although the Vermont Book Shop carries no textbooks, it has a strong following of students from nearby colleges, who, on lazy afternoons, can be found browsing for anything from Tolkien to Salinger and from Bradbury to Mailer. They usually find something. Blair's selection of books is based on his long experience with the book business (he once worked for Doubleday's in New York), an intimate knowledge of his customers, and an almost mystical literary and sales acumen as to what makes a good and desirable book. "A lot of people think a bookseller's life is not demanding—that booksellers do nothing but read books all

196

day," says Blair. "This is far from the truth. We deal with literally hundreds of sources each day (advertisements, publishers' catalogs, book salesmen, customers' requests, etc.) and must decide which new items will be in demand and which will not." Blair's instincts have proven to be astute: poet Robert Frost, a constant visitor, often said that Blair knew which book he wanted as he entered the store, before he even asked for it.

The Vermont Book Shop not only sells books, but publishes them as well. Issuing titles under the imprint of Vermont Books, the store has published such limited editions as *Vermont Sampler*, *A Matter of Fifty Houses*, *Vermont Neighbors*, and *Mountain Township*. Blair's own book, also published by Vermont Books, *Books and Bedlam*, a collection of parodies, bogus letters, and humorous pieces centered in a Vermont bookstore, received a rave review from the late Bennett Cerf, who called it "fresh and engaging humor."

In addition to books of all kinds, the Vermont Book Shop also carries a huge supply of record albums, some greeting cards, and an ample stock of maps and posters. A special Christmas catalog is mailed annually. Customers can be included on the mailing list by simply requesting it. Visa and Master Charge are accepted.

Blair relates the philosophy of the Vermont Book Shop: "Books are read for two reasons, information and entertainment. But there aren't many books a person can read without learning something."

38 Main Street, Middlebury, Vermont 05753; Tel. 802-388-2061. Hours: Monday–Saturday, 8:30 A.M.–5:30 P.M.

Of the many worlds which man did not receive as a gift of nature, but created with his own spirit, the world of books is the greatest.

HERMAN HESSE

Washington

MONTANA BOOKS, INC.

**SEATTLE
WASHINGTON**

In the Wallingford district of Seattle, just west of the university district, stands one of the most beautiful bookstores in the country. On one side is an art-deco wall of glass; a glassed-in office hovers on a balcony overhead. Almost everything else is of wood: walls, shelving, trim, all skillfully handmade, apparently with loving care. Fiction is housed in an upstairs balcony where customers can while away hours with no disturbance.

Montana Books is the joint creation of Peter Miller, Raymond Mungo, and Judy Thompson, who cofounded it in 1973. It carries a small but carefully selected stock of books. As Ray Mungo says, "It's a personal bookstore, a particular selection, small but far-ranging." They carry only new books, paperbacks and hardcover, with collections of small press books, new fiction, poetry, and how-to-do-it books.

The store has recently gone into the publishing business, reissuing Aldous Huxley's long out-of-print book, *The Art of Seeing* (with a foreword by Huxley's widow); the current project is a fiction and nonfiction series of "far-out writers."

Mungo says, "The environment is literary," and it is; the whole shop gives the air of a literary salon. Many writers drop in from time to time, to talk, to browse, or to give a reading.

Montana Books is a party-giver, and its literary readings have become slightly notorious in the area, with free cognac and lots of congenial company. February brings the annual Winterlude Water Reading, an event worth attending if you're in the area at that time (contact the store for details).

The shop stocks cards and maps, and sometimes holds art

exhibits. There is no charge for being put on their mailing list; just send the store your name and address. Montana Books will special order books for its customers, and it holds sales and other special events from time to time.

Now that the store has become so popular, it has opened a branch store in the heart of Pioneer Square, the downtown waterfront section of Seattle. Called Miller & Mungo, the branch embodies the spirit of its mother store and carries the same "small but far-ranging" selection of fine books, with the same areas of specialization: literary and utilitarian.

The corporate motto of both stores may offer some small explanation of what they are, and what they want to be. It's a line from Henry James: "One should never be both corrupt and dreary."

Montana Books, Inc., 1716 North 45th Street, Seattle, Washington 98103; Tel. 206-633-0811. Miller & Mungo, St. Charles Hotel Building, 81 South Washington Street, Seattle, Washington 98104; Tel. 206-623-5563. Hours (both stores): Monday–Friday, 10:00 A.M.–9:00 P.M.; Saturday, 10:00 A.M.–7:00 P.M.; Sunday, 10:00 A.M.–5:00 P.M.

UNIVERSITY BOOK STORE

SEATTLE WASHINGTON

One of the largest university bookstores in the United States, second only to the Harvard Coop, the University Book Store may be the best. It certainly is the best in the West. The store is brilliantly stocked, and is a down-to-business, no-frills bookstore where it is possible to find at least half of the forty thousand new titles that are published in this country every year. In all, the store carries some sixty thousand different titles.

Founded in 1900, the store has expanded slowly over the years, and it wasn't until 1977 that it finally erected a new addition, a $2 million annex that doubled the area available for selling general books.

The University Bookstore carries a profusely stocked line of new paperback and hardbound, fiction and nonfiction books, including sections of college textbooks, technical books, and foreign-language books; and the store's manager, Leroy Soper, claims that the children's book department might very well be "the best anywhere." There is also a used textbook section. The store issues a Christmas catalog and a monthly newsletter (which tells about new books in the general book department), both of which can be had for the asking. Also sold are art works, engineering and student supplies, sporting goods, men's and women's clothing, records, typewriters, cameras, calculators, and gifts. The store accepts Master Charge and Visa credit cards.

Says Soper: "We carry such a broad and enormous stock to cover all subject areas, in an attempt to satisfy all tastes and interests. We think we succeed."

4326 University Way NE, Seattle, Washington 98105; Tel. 206-634-3400. Hours: Monday–Saturday, 8:45 A.M.–5:30 P.M.; Thursday, 8:45 A.M.–9:00 P.M.

THE BOOK NOOK   TACOMA
WASHINGTON

There is a huge, stained-glass sign with the name of the store over the main, double-door entrance to the Book Nook. But if you think that the word "nook" implies a small store, you'll be surprised. The Book Nook is one of the largest, best-stocked bookstores in the city and carries up to 200,000 books at any given time. Located in a beautiful suburb of Tacoma, this shop is guarded by the majestic Mt. Rainier, which it is possible to see from the rear window.

Founded in 1961 by Tom and Sandy Morris, the Book Nook is what could be described as a "browser's" store. Not particularly neat or well ordered, long and rambling, nevertheless the shop quickly gives one the feeling that the book that is being sought will be found. It usually is. In addition to a large selection of general books, with good collections of science fiction, children's books, military history, cookbooks, and books on boating, the store also carries German-language paperbacks, a large selection of British titles, and a goodly number of magazines, including some in French and Spanish. There are frequent autograph parties, and book fairs several times each year.

Other book dealers in Tacoma look upon the Book Nook as the store of last resort, sending their customers there if they don't have a particular title. Because of its size and volume, the Book Nook also acts as a mini-distributor and often supplies other bookstores with titles that they need in a hurry. Recently, the store opened a children's bookstore, about two thousand square feet attached to the Nook, almost doubling its size.

Although there is no mailing list, the store will gladly service mail-order requests. The most unusual sale of late was an order from the Aleutian Islands in Alaska for a book on refrigeration! The Book Nook filled it with aplomb.

10303 Gravelly Lake Drive, Tacoma, Washington 98499; Tel. 206-584-4105. Hours: Monday–Friday, 10:00 A.M.–9:00 P.M.; Saturday, 10:00 A.M.–6:00 P.M.; Sunday, 12:00 Noon–5:00 P.M.

I love to lose myself in other men's minds. When I am not walking, I am reading. I cannot sit and think; books think for me.

CHARLES LAMB

THE WALLA WALLA
BOOK SHOP

WALLA WALLA
WASHINGTON

Two sisters, Alberta and Almira Quinn, founded this shop twenty-five years ago. Then, in January 1977, they sold the shop—to two other sisters, Donna P. Jones and Barbara P. Campbell. The store has one employee and specializes in old books, children's books, unusual cards, and stationery. It stocks books of all types, both new and used, hard and soft cover, fiction and nonfiction. A very active store, the Walla Walla Book Shop handles special orders for customers, carries old books on consignment, holds autographing parties, and generally keeps things moving in—and out!

Everything has its compensations. The Walla Walla Book Shop is right on the main street, but has plenty of parking space in back. The proprietress explains that "as a small business, I can't supply all the books that everyone asks for, but I try to fill the needs of my customers and try to maintain some semblance of being a unique store."

Our assessment is that although the Walla Walla Book Shop is not a grandiose operation, it is one that is dedicated to service. If you find yourself in Walla Walla, by all means stop in and say hello—you'll get a warm greeting in return.

23 E. Main Street, Walla Walla, Washington 99362; Tel. 509-525-2803. Hours: Monday–Saturday, 9:30 A.M.–5:30 P.M.; Friday till 9:00 P.M.

Wisconsin

HARRY W. SCHWARTZ BOOK SHOP

MILWAUKEE WISCONSIN

Half a century of bookselling makes this store a bibliophile's paradise. Founded by Harry W. Schwartz in 1927, this shop is now operated by A. David Schwartz, and boasts a complement of sixteen employees. New as well as used books are sold, and the store maintains an in-depth stock of titles that cover a broad spectrum of reader interest. While the stock is general in nature, there is some specialization; in addition to the fiction and nonfiction titles, technical and business books, as well as those on medicine and social criticism, get special attention. Books are both hard and soft bound, and when asked how many books are kept in stock, the harried Mr. Schwartz answered "God knows."

The bright, "booky" staff will search for special out-of-print books at a customer's request. The store also services mail-order requests, and customers can write and ask to be placed on the mailing list, at no charge. Indeed, according to Mr. Schwartz, the shop does everything for its customers, "except babysitting."

The shop celebrated its fiftieth anniversary with authors' visits and readings. It's a pleasant store to browse in, and lends itself readily to readings. The decor is attractive, with high, beamed ceilings restored from the original 1890s architecture.

There are no other offerings such as cards, maps, games, and toys—this bookstore sells only books, to service the entire community. It accepts Master Charge and BankAmericard.

Asked about his philosophy as a bookseller, Mr. Schwartz became reflective: "Books are tools for social change and we booksellers have historically acted in the role of social activists. I feel that it is a fundamental part of the bookseller's experience—buying, displaying, promoting, and if necessary, giving away books with positive impact."

440 W. Wisconsin Avenue, Milwaukee, Wisconsin 53203; Tel. 414-272-2700. Hours: Monday and Thursday, 9:30 A.M.–9:00 P.M.; Tuesday, Wednesday, Friday, Saturday, 9:30 A.M.–6:00 P.M.

A book is good company. It is full of conversation without loquacity. It comes to your longing with full instruction, but pursues you never.

HENRY WARD BEECHER

Canada

A DIFFERENT DRUMMER BOOKS

BURLINGTON ONTARIO

"A bookseller's function," says Al Cummings, "is to get books to people as quickly as possible and at the best possible price, sometimes with the help of publishers, and sometimes in spite of them. In the process of doing this, we strive to make a contribution to our community and have as much fun as possible. So far, we've been successful."

The store was founded in 1970 by Al Cummings and is now jointly owned by him and John Richardson. It employs seven people, stocks some twenty-five thousand books, general in nature. It sells new books only, both hard and soft cover, fiction and nonfiction. The Different Drummer special orders books for customers from all over the world, has its own gift certificates and charge accounts, and will gift-wrap. The store also undertakes book searching at no charge.

The owners have held autograph parties in the store and author evenings at the local library, and they have had as many as 375 in attendance. They also hold a series of author breakfasts/brunches at the local golf club. The mailing list is extensive, and the store does regular mailings to customers, many of whom live in the United States. The owners find that the business they do with U.S. libraries and bookstores, filling all their Canadian needs, is growing in importance. Should you want to be added to their mailing list, simply send in your name and address—there's no charge for this. And the store will service mail orders from anyplace for any book in print.

Who are the customers at Different Drummer? They come from a middle-income community of about 110,000 people with broad-ranging interests.

The shop is housed in a seventy-five-year-old brick building that was completely gutted, all interior walls and staircases having been removed. The interior was replaced with an open, spacious design with a balcony and an airway that rises some thirty feet to the building's crown. Both children and adult sitting areas are provided, and classical music is piped in. In the plant and craft books section you'll find a small greenhouse. All of this is carefully supervised by the two cats, Marble and Cricket.

Peter C. Newman, author of many Canadian best sellers and editor of *Maclean's Magazine*, visited the store, and on leaving, he said, "You've created a rare oasis of civilization—I wish there were a hundred of you in Canada."

Farley Mowat, after a hard day of promoting his book to the press and public, which included an evening at the Burlington Library, called Al Cummings "a bloody slave driver!" But before he left, he autographed a copy of his book for Al, prefacing the autograph "with affection."

If you find yourself heading toward Toronto, London, or Stratford at Niagara Falls, you'll find this shop less than three minutes off the Queen Elizabeth Way. All they sell here is books, and the store accepts Visa and Master Charge. Visiting A Different Drummer is not a shopping trip, it's a literary and aesthetic experience.

513 Locust Street, Burlington, Ontario, Canada L7S 1V3; Tel. 416-639-0925. Hours: Monday–Saturday, 10:00 A.M.–6:00 P.M.; Thursday and Friday, until 9:00 P.M.

LONGHOUSE BOOK SHOP LTD.　　TORONTO ONTARIO

With the growing interest in Canadian publishing and the increasing pride of Canadians in their own authors and their own literature, Beth Appeldoorn defied the format of longstanding bookstores to open Canada's first all-Canadian bookshop. To complicate matters, the shop is on expensive Yonge Street, fairly surrounded by other, long-established bookstores. The critics wagged their knowing heads and predicted that such a specialized store in such a high-rent district could not long survive.

That was in 1972, and Beth and coowner Susan Sandler now have only one regret: not enough room. The well-ordered store carries twenty thousand titles. They're all new books, both hardbound and paperbacks, fiction and nonfiction. All adult books are written and published by Canadians. Naturally, many of them are also concerned with Canadiana, and the store has a unique collection of books about Canada's native peoples, as well as a fascinating selection of original native Indian art. The store also stocks all Canadian textbooks.

Interestingly, the only exception to this deliberate chauvinism occurs in the area of children's books. Canadian books are, of course, offered here, but Appeldoorn feels that there is not yet a large enough body of Canadian children's works, particularly for young children, and so she fills out this department with an excellent international collection of children's books and materials. The result is one of the best selections of children's books in Toronto.

The motivating force behind the idea for an all-Canada bookstore (which now has its imitators in other cities) is not, herself, a native Canadian. Beth Appledoorn was a Dutch medical student when she flew to Canada to stay for a year. That was about fourteen years ago. After touring the country, she found herself out of money, so she walked into a Cole's bookstore in suburban Toronto and took a job as an eighty-five-cents-an-hour clerk. She became a trade buyer within three months, moved to the main store at Yonge and Charles Streets, and finished her first year in bookselling with a commitment to it as a career and to Canada as her new, permanent home.

She switched to a job as main buyer at the York University bookstore, where she eventually became manager. In her seven years there, she developed an intense desire to open her own store, which, like European bookstores, would support the writers of the country. "When I first arrived in Canada," she recalls, "there were small sections at the back of stores marked Canadiana . . . no other country treated its own authors in this manner."

She and Sandler opened the Longhouse in May of 1972 and nursed it for two years until it came into its own. The store is a showcase for Canadian authors (no U.S. best sellers), and it aims to keep all its titles in stock.

The Longhouse is part of the Yonge Street book strip. Customers go shopping in the various bookstores, choosing the best of each specialty. But for books Canadian, they come to the Longhouse. It stocks every book that McClelland & Stewart has in print, and searches out new titles from small or obscure houses.

"This is not a self-service bookstore," Beth says, in explaining the store's philosophy. "We like to tell people about books." And to do this, the staff have made themselves highly knowledgeable about their ever-expanding stock. Their reputation has grown so that even Canadian publishers come to them, seeking their opinions on new publishing ideas.

The staff provides many services for the store's customers, in addition to advice on books. They will special order books, search for out-of-print titles, and send mail orders. They prepare a catalog, and customers can receive a copy by requesting to be put on the store's mailing list. The Longhouse also has an extensive mail-order business, sending books to individuals, libraries, and schools all over the world. It accepts Chargex.

Canadian authors and poets use the shop as a meeting place and enjoy the opportunity to talk with their readers. They also visit during the store's frequent autograph parties.

The store is a bit of a marvel of careful planning. Space has been used to great advantage, and the books are organized by topic, with the most popular titles easily accessible.

It's a great place to browse, no matter what country you're from.

630 Yonge Street, Toronto, Ontario, Canada M4Y 1Z8; Tel. 416-921-9995 or 921-0389. Hours: Monday–Friday, 10:00 A.M.–6:00 P.M.; Saturday, 10:00 A.M.–5:00 P.M.

UNIVERSITY BOOKROOM   TORONTO
                                     ONTARIO

Located in the middle of the beautiful campus of the University of Toronto, the University Bookroom is the largest academic bookstore in the Commonwealth—it has well over 100,000 books in stock—and has one of the most complete selections of scholarly journals in the country.

The store is a pleasant one and has tables with umbrellas outside for those who want to read their purchases immediately after securing them. The store advertises that "browsing is encouraged" inside. In addition to books and periodicals, it sells stationery supplies and records. The staff members do book searching, free of charge, for out-of or in-print books and will special order any book that they can find. The store also issues specialized catalogs—its medical book catalog is excellent—from time to time, and anyone can be placed on the list simply by requesting it.

John D. Taylor, the general manager of the store, is a book-lover, par excellence. "My favorite pastime is checking the receiving area to see what books have come in. It's like Christmas every day, as we open the parcels of new books. It seems almost immoral to me to be actually paid for operating a bookstore."

209

63a St. George Street, Toronto, Ontario, Canada M5S 1A6; Tel. 416-978-7088. Hours: Monday–Friday, 8:45 A.M.–6:00 P.M.

Some books are undeservedly forgotten; none are undeservedly remembered.

W. H. AUDEN

BAKKA   TORONTO
ONTARIO

The Bakka Science Fiction and Fantasy Shoppe is an interesting store. The store was founded in 1972 and was the first all–science-fiction shop in North America (several have started since then). It is mighty successful and adds a nice touch to Toronto, a city known for its unique and plentiful bookshops.

Charles McKee and Raymond Alexander, owners, make an attempt to carry not only all books covering science fiction and fantasy, but also related art, movie memorabilia, comics, posters, and prints. They also stock—when they can—a limited number of relatively rare items, but both complain that these items never stay long enough to be cherished by them. They're talking about such items as the first book of Lovecraft or *Action 1*, the initial comic book devoted to Superman.

Bakka issues a fully illustrated 160-page magazine catalog on both subjects, mystery and science fiction, several times a year. It's an ambitious publication, crammed with material for nostalgia buffs. The cost is $2.00 for SF and $1.50 for mystery issues.

McKee explains that his philosophy of bookselling is really not to be a bookseller at all: he considers his stores an extension

210

of his home, a living room in which all of his friends and would-be friends gather; he sees his role more as a caretaker of a special genre rather than as a bookdealer and does everything he can to spread the word and to bring science fiction and fantasy to a wider audience.

282–286 Queen St. W, Toronto, Ontario, Canada M5V 2A1; Tel. 416-361-1161. Hours: Monday–Saturday, 10:30 A.M.–6:00 P.M.

The Chains

Although there have been chains of bookstores in this country for many years, they have been a growing phenomenon for the past decade. Today, books sold in the chains comprise the greatest proportion of annual sales for publishers. Customers now know that if they go to a chain bookstore, chances are it will have the book they are seeking, perhaps even at a discounted price. The owners of smaller bookstores feel that they cannot compete with the chains, which have the ability to buy books from publishers at larger discounts because they purchase in huge quantities and can consequently pass the savings on to the customer. The small bookstore owner also cannot afford to maintain as large an inventory, nor can he advertise his book with full-page advertisements in newspapers as the chains do.

There are some bookmen who predict the doom of the small, privately owned bookstore because of the increased popularity and success of the chains. Small bookstores, however, have some advantages over the chains. They can afford to give time to a customer, establish a rapport, and get to know their customers and what kinds of books they want. They also can stock non–best sellers and books that the chains cannot afford to keep in inventory because they might not sell enough copies. Finally, the small bookstore can give personal service in a way that the chains find difficult, if not impossible, to match. In many ways, the chains and the small booksellers complement each other, the one supplying the book-buyer with what the other cannot.

So long as the small bookstores continue to offer personal service, they will thrive, and they need not fear the growth of the chains. The chains cannot be overlooked, moreover, as excellent bookstores in themselves, for browsing *and* buying. Almost invariably well-stocked, efficiently staffed, brightly lit, and easy on the pocketbook, they have served to bolster book-buying, to reach large numbers of people who otherwise might not read. Accordingly, we list our favorites.

Kroch's and Brentano's, a chain of eighteen stores in the Chicago area, was founded in 1907. Carl Kroch, son of the original owner, is currently the president of the company, whose flagship store is located at 29 South Wabash in Chicago. It is a particular favorite of Chicagoans and is considered by many book experts to be the best bookstore in America. The store has a rich literary history, with virtually every major American author having visited it over the years. The Midwest authors, such as Ernest Hemingway, Saul Bellow, Willard Motley, and Studs Terkel, have always seemed to be store regulars.

Kroch's and Brentano's carries a complete selection of new and backlist titles in all categories. Its art book department is probably the most outstanding of any general bookstore in the country. In addition, it has a comprehensive stock of business, science and technical books, and a popular collection of cards, calendars, prints, and gifts.

B. Dalton Booksellers, whose headquarters are in Minneapolis, opened its first store in a shopping center in 1966 and today is the largest bookseller in the world in sales volume, with over 300 stores in thirty-nine states. Their stores are in malls, business districts, and "strip centers," wherever there are people who buy and read books. The average store carries over thirty thousand titles, selling strictly books, new and remaindered, hardbound and paperbound, "from wall to wall, floor to ceiling," according to Dick Fontaine, who is Dalton's vice-president of merchandising. "We really believe bookselling is undermarketed. Many people would buy books and read books if we could bring the books to them. If you can bring bookstores to high-traffic areas, you can connect many books with many people," he says.

The Baptist Book Store chain consists of sixty-five stores in twenty-four states, employing well over 500 people. The philosophy of the store is direct and forthright: to assist the Baptist Sunday School Board in its attempt to bring people to God through the study of the teachings of Jesus Christ. All stores carry books and other materials that they hope will help people meet their basic spiritual and emotional needs. They also assist Southern Baptist churches in their work. Their headquarters are at 127 Ninth Avenue North in Nashville, Tennessee.

Bibles of just about every sort imaginable are the most popular items of the Baptist Book Stores, and one can find looseleaf Bibles, large-print Bibles, verse Bibles, reference Bibles, annotated Bibles, "modern English" Bibles, Bibles for the bride, Bibles for children, Bibles for special places, Bible atlases, Bible dictionaries, and hundreds of books that are commentaries to aid in the study of the Bible. The stores carry books for ministers and Sunday School teachers, books of spiritual and practical advice for the church's members, books and all kinds of music, church supplies, and biographies of religious leaders. They also carry greeting cards, stationery items, and even church furniture. Some fifteen thousand items are listed in their illustrated catalog, which will be sent, free of charge, for the asking.

Slightly different in approach is the *Logos* chain, sixty bookstores with a mission—to bring books with a Judeo-Christian viewpoint to believers and nonbelievers alike, especially within the academic community. Started in 1968 in Ann Arbor, Michigan, the chain sells books, cards, gifts, posters, and records that "deal with matters of human concern, com-

215

municate truth and grace, and promote wholeness in personal lives and society." Each store fits its community, yet belongs to the Association of Logos Bookstores, a service organization that helps establish and stock each store.

C. S. Lewis is a favorite author at Logos: "We praise every publisher who publishes his work," says James Carlson, executive director of the chain. Carlson, discussing the problems of stocking his stores, made the point that they do not sell textbooks, books on Eastern religion, astrology, Edgar Cayce, or the occult. "We try to stock—and encourage students to read—books that are responsibly written on subjects of both personal and social concern. Our stock includes literally hundreds of books on the relationship between God and man. We want students to develop a total world-and-life-view of this relationship. That's a big order, and we are never fully successful."

U.S. Bookstores, which are operated by the Government Printing Office, sell millions of books each year in some twenty-four locations, the principal outlet being the GPO office at 710 North Capitol Street, Washington, D.C. Of the twenty-four thousand titles currently in print, it is possible to buy inexpensive books and pamphlets on such subjects as infant care, assassination plots involving foreign leaders, sources of natural energy, and government land for sale. The stores do issue book lists, and one can be placed on the mailing list by writing to Washington. Stores are located in all the principal cities of the United States, including New York, Chicago, Los Angeles, Boston, Philadelphia, Detroit, and Dallas.

Waldenbooks has a total of 436 stores. A. G. Coons, the company's president, is attempting to broaden the availability of books in the country by a significant factor. "We serve

216

localities that have been unserved by bookstores before," he says. "Our business, like the publisher's, is to give the people what they want in interesting, high-quality, and instructive books whether it be hardcover, paperback, or medium cover and whether it is high or low in price. The majority of our stores are in mall locations; we've expanded as a function of the growth of malls in America. It's our perception that there is a significant difference between getting into a car to consciously drive to a store in a nonmall location, and simply being in a mall shopping, and dropping in to the bookstore."

With headquarters in Stamford, Connecticut, Waldenbooks continues to open new bookstores, each with an enormous stock, attractively displayed, and each selling new, sale, and remaindered bargain books.

"It's my perception that we have not adversely affected the small bookseller," Coons concludes. "If anything, we've helped. I've talked to many booksellers and publishers and they agree."

Other Favorite Bookstores

The bookstores listed on the following pages are an amalgam of used book stores, shops that sell only new books, rare book dealers and specialists, and some bookstores that combine all of these services and elements. The hours and days that these stores are open are not listed, and it would be wise to call before a visit is made, since many dealers, especially those who deal in rare books, are open only for limited hours during any given week and some are open only by appointment.

ARIZONA

GUIDON BOOKS

7117 Main Street
Scottsdale, Arizona 85251
Tel: 602-945-8811

Used and out-of-print books on Arizona, Western Americana, Civil War.

ROSE TREE BOOK AND ANTIQUE SHOP

Tombstone, Arizona 85638
Tel: 602-457-3326

Stocks large quantity of books on Arizona and the town of Tombstone. Catalogs issued.

CALIFORNIA

EVERYBODY'S

311 W. Sixth St.
Los Angeles, California 90014
Tel: 213-623-6234

Over 100,000 used books, 2 million back-issue magazines, movie stills, comic books.

ALPHABOOKS

18046 Ventura Blvd.
Encino, California 91316
Tel: 213-344-6365

Owners Ray and Betty Vasin keep a well-stocked collection of scarce, used, and out-of-print books, encyclopedias, back-issue magazines.

CARAVAN BOOK STORE

605 S. Grand Avenue
Los Angeles, California 90017
Tel: 213-626-9944

*Fine and rare book specialists in
Californiana, American military
history, early aviation books,
railroads, and political memorabilia.*

OLD MONTEREY BOOK COMPANY

136 Bonifacio Place
Monterey, California 93940
Tel: 408-372-3111

*Over 100,000 out-of-print titles,
specializing in illustrated books,
Western Americana, limited editions, etc. Lists issued.*

BILLIARD ARCHIVES

1113 Dodson Avenue
San Pedro, California 90732
Tel: 213-833-4518

*Used and out-of-print books, pic-
tures, posters, and memorabilia
on billiards, pool and snooker.*

THE BOOK CELLAR

122 Orangefair Mall
Fullerton, California 92632
Tel: 714-879-9420

*Located three miles north of Dis-
neyland. Specialists in fine and
rare illustrated books, art and
erotica, folklore and mythology,
children's books. Send $2.50 to
David Cormany for copy of latest
catalog.*

BRENTWOOD BOOKSHOP

11975 San Vicente Blvd.
Los Angeles, California 90049
Tel: 213-476-6263

*A good general store servicing
the Bel-Air and Brentwood area.
Good section of quality trade
paperbacks.*

THE THUNDERBIRD BOOKSHOP

W. Carmel Valley Road
Carmel, California 93921
Tel: 408-624-1803

*Store was founded in 1961. Has a
stock of 20,000 books. Owners
Jim and Corenne Smith serve
lunch and coffee on the patio.*

HERITAGE BOOKSHOP

847 North La Cienega Boulevard
Los Angeles, California 90069
Tel: 213-659-3674

*Rare books and manuscripts,
first editions.*

FIREPLACE BOOKSHOP

2 N. Valley Plaza
Chico, California 95926
Tel: 916-342-2479

Carries hardbound books and paperbacks. Specializes in cooking and nutrition, Western Americana, and juveniles.

CHATTERTON'S

1818 N. Vermont Avenue
Los Angeles, California 90027
Tel: 213-664-3882

Known as a poet's bookstore, though good on most subjects. Largest selection of literary and poetry magazines in Southern California. As big as a barn, with skylights.

A CHANGE OF HOBBIT

1371 Westwood Blvd.
Los Angeles, California 90024
Tel: 213-473-2873

Science-fiction and fantasy. Store is run by Sherry Gottlieb, who calls herself The Hobbitch *on her personal bookmarkers.*

KISCH BOOK SHOP

25½ W. Cenon Perdido St.
Santa Barbara, California 93101
Tel: 805-962-4801

General new and used books, hardbound and paperback, with a strong emphasis on science fiction, fantasy, mystery, and literature. This is a store to go to if you can't find what you're looking for anywhere else.

THE HOLMES BOOK COMPANY

274 Fourteenth Street
Oakland, California 94612
Tel: 415-893-6860

One of the West's oldest and largest stores specializing in used, out-of-print, and rare books concerning Western Americana, California, and books by California authors.

PAPA BACH

11317 Santa Monica Blvd.
West Los Angeles, California 90025
Tel: 213-478-2374

First bookstore in L.A. for poets and leftists. Funky atmosphere. Publishes Bachy, *its own literary magazine. In addition to radical books, has a good children's section.*

JOHN HOWELL BOOKS

434 Post St.
San Francisco, California 94102
Tel: 415-781-7795

Established in 1912. Carries used, out-of-print, and rare books of all kinds, specializing in Western Americana, incunabula, art books, science, and medicine.

TILLMAN PLACE BOOKSHOP

8 Tillman Place
San Francisco, California 94108
Tel: 415-392-4668

This personal store, which carries general books, is located in an historical section of San Francisco and housed in a building with an old English facade. Inside there are dark walnut fixtures.

LENNIE'S BOOK NOOK

8125 W. 3rd St.
Los Angeles, California 90048
Tel: 213-651-5584

Unusual used books bought and sold concerning the cinema, theater, biography.

BARRY R. LEVIN

2253 Westwood Blvd.
Los Angeles, California 90064
Tel: 213-474-5611

Used, scarce, and out-of-print editions concerning science fiction and fantasy.

RICHARD HANSEN

12410 New Airport Road
Auburn, California 95603
Tel: 916-885-4878

Used and out-of-print books on California.

THE IMAGE AND THE MYTH

9843 Santa Monica Blvd.
Beverly Hills, California 90212
Tel: 213-553-5728

Used and scarce works by surrealists, limited editions and 20th-century art books.

LION BOOKSHOP

3422 Balboa
San Francisco, California 94121
Tel: 415-221-5522

Specialists in out-of-print literature, especially the 1920s and 1930s, history, biography, and the performing arts.

NEVIN E. LYON

11552 Hartsook St.
North Hollywood, California
  91601
Tel: 213-766-0044

*Old and rare and out-of-print
books concerning dogs, breed-
ing, kennels.*

NEEDHAM BOOK FINDERS

2317 Westwood Blvd.
Los Angeles, California 90064
Tel: 213-475-9553

*A good browsing store with over
60,000 used books in all fields.
Provides a fast, effective search
service.*

THE SHTETL

7606 Beverly Boulevard
Los Angeles, California 90036
Tel: 213-932-8992

*Stocks used books of Jewish in-
terest. Catalogs issued.*

THIS OLD HOUSE BOOKSHOP

5399 W. Holt Boulevard
Montclair, California 91763
Tel: 714-624-5144

*Used books on literature, West-
ern and California authors, and
general nostalgia.*

BANBURY BOOK SHOP

20929 Ventura Blvd.
Woodland Hills, California
  91364
Tel: 213-348-1644

*An excellent general bookstore
with an outstanding children's
section. Specializing in gift-
wrapping, personal service is
their first concern.*

JUNE O'SHEA BOOKS

6222 San Vicente Blvd.
Los Angeles, California 90048
Tel: 213-935-7872

*Used, rare, and out-of-print
books concerning psychology,
psychiatry, and criminology.*

SUN DANCE BOOKS

1520 N. Crescent Heights
Hollywood, California 90046
Tel: 213-654-2383

*Antiquarian book specialists in
the fields of Mexico, Latin
America. By appointment only.*

COLORADO

HATCH'S BOOKSTORE

Cinderella City Shopping
  Center
Englewood, Colorado 80110
Tel: 303-761-2550

*A good general bookstore with
many branches throughout Colorado.*

WRITERS BOOKSHOP

1365 Logan St.
Denver, Colorado 80203
Tel: 303-861-1234

*Specializes in books on writing,
technical and reference books.
Manager is Donald E. Bower.*

CONNECTICUT

EDWARD ANDREWS

42 Sea Beach Drive
Stamford, Connecticut 06902
Tel: 203-359-3087

*Specialists in used and old books
on 19th-century American fiction, with emphasis on Hawthorne, Melville, Whittier,
Thoreau, Lowell, Craddock, etc.*

MARTIN D. GOLD

Route 128

West Cornwall, Connecticut
  06796
Tel: 203-672-6333

*One of the largest selections of
out-of-print books in New England.*

WALTER E. HALLBERG

525 Main St.
Hartford, Connecticut 06103
Tel: 203-233-8937

*Used, rare, out-of-print books
concerning Connecticut.*

FLORIDA

THE CHARLOTTE ST. SHOP

32 Charlotte St.
St. Augustine, Florida 32084
Tel: 305-829-2361

*Antiquarian books on Americana
and Florida.*

GAUL'S BOOK STORE

Coral Ridge Shopping Plaza
Fort Lauderdale, Florida 33306
Tel: 305-565-3411

A good general store that has been thriving for over 30 years. In addition to being well stocked with books of all kinds, it has an excellent record collection.

BOOK STORE OF NAPLES

1300 Third St. S.
Naples, Florida 33940
Tel: 813-262-3851

An excellent general bookstore with good sections of fiction, gardening, cookery, nutrition, Floridiana, the sea, photography, and sports. Also has a used book section.

MICKLER'S FLORIDIANA

Chuluota, Florida 32766
Tel: 305-365-3636

Carries all kinds of books relating to Florida, especially out-of-print and scarce titles. By appointment only.

RALPH CURTIS BOOKS

2633 Adams St.
Hollywood, Florida 33020
Tel: 305-925-4639

Used and new books on wildlife, mammals, and birds. Issues catalogs.

IVES BOOK STORE

Edison Mall
Fort Meyers, Florida 33901
Tel: 813-936-4525

Excellent general bookstore of new books, run by an engaging couple, Frank and Mona Ives.

OLD BOOK SHOP

3110 Commodore Plaza
Miami, Florida 33133
Tel: 305-661-4913

Located in the chic Coconut Grove section, this store is great for browsing; its used book section is excellent.

GEORGIA

HARVEY DAN ABRAMS BOOK-SELLERS

3878 Vermont Road, N.E.
Atlanta, Georgia 30319
Tel: 404-233-2538

Used book specialists in Georgia and Southern Americana, Confederate books, first and limited editions.

LEE STREET BOOK SHOP

1513 Lee Street
Brunswick, Georgia 31520
Tel: 912-265-7836

A small, although well-stocked, personal store on coastal Georgia.

E. SHAVER, FINE BOOKS

326 Bull Street
Savannah, Georgia 31401
Tel: 912-234-7257

Located in the heart of historic downtown Savannah, this store stocks scarce books about Georgia, the South, the Civil War, and Savannah.

HOUND DOG PRESS BOOK SHOP

340 West Ponce de Leon Avenue
Decatur, Georgia 30030
Tel: 404-373-2291

ILLINOIS

JUNCTION BOOK SHOP

Junction City Shopping Center
Peoria, Illinois 61614
Tel: 309-691-4633

Owner and manager Aileen Rutherford keeps approximately 11,000 volumes in stock, consisting of hardcover and paperback books. Sells children's books, adult games, and greeting cards.

OAK STREET BOOK SHOP

54 East Oak St.
Chicago, Illinois 60611
Tel: 312-642-3070

Remember the film, Harry and Tonto, *when Art Carney visits his daughter, who owns a bookstore in Chicago? This is it.*

One of the best smallish bookstores in Chicago, it carries a plentiful stock of hardback, paperbound, and remainders. The emphasis is on art and the performing arts, with an additionally excellent selection of children's books. Owned and managed by Arlene Wimmer and Carol Stoll.

KENNEDY'S BOOKSHOP

1911 Central Street
Evanston, Illinois 60204
Tel: 312-864-4449 and
    312-475-2481

Joan Kennedy Wilson, the manager of the store, keeps well stocked with standard and scholarly books of all kinds.

226

IOWA

REED LIBRARY OF THE FOOT
AND ANKLE

6000 Waterbury Circle
Des Moines, Iowa 50312
Tel: 515-277-5756

This organization sells, trades, and buys any book or journal about feet, podiatry, shoes, and footwear. Has many back issues of podiatric publications for sale.

KENTUCKY

OLD LOUISVILLE BOOKS

46 W. Oak Street
Louisville, Kentucky 40203
Tel: 502-637-6411

As the name of this store implies, its great specialty is books on Kentucky: its history, its counties, cities, and geography.

LOUISIANA

BAYOU BOOKS

1005 Monroe St.
Gretna, Louisiana 70053
Tel: 504-368-1171

Manager Joyce Bilbray carries a large stock of used, rare, and out-of-print books on Louisiana. Catalogs issued.

MAINE

DOWNEAST BOOK SERVICE

Pierce's Pond Road
Penobscot, Maine 04476
Tel: 201-326-4771

Owner Tom Stotler keeps a good stock of scarce 19th-century juveniles, books on Americana and science, and first editions. Catalogs issued.

EDGECOMB BOOK BARN

Cross Point Road
North Edgecomb, Maine 04556
Tel: 207-882-7278

Carries used books, prints, and paintings. A good store for the difficult to find.

227

MARYLAND

THE OLD PRINTED WORD

3808 Howard Avenue
Kensington, Maryland 20795
Tel: 301-933-7253

An antiquarian bookstore that carries old books, prints, and newspapers of general Americana.

GORDON'S BOOKSELLERS

8 East Baltimore St.
Baltimore, Maryland 21202
Tel: 301-685-7313

Owner Melvin Gordon has six branches in the hub of the city, near theaters, stores, transportation. His stores all have a good selection of hardbound and paperbound books, new and remaindered.

MASSACHUSETTS

GOODSPEED'S

18 Beacon St. & 2 Milk St.
Boston, Massachusetts 02108
Tel: 617-523-5970

Two enormous shops carrying used and old books in all fields. "Anything that's a book" is their motto.

ODYSSEY

29 College Street
South Hadley, Massachusetts
　01075
Tel: 413-534-7307

Housed in a white clapboard building opposite Mt. Holyoke, in a beautiful setting, this store is owned by Romeo Grenier, a pharmacist with a love and great knowledge of books. The store has an excellent general collection and a good selection of scholarly books.

228

HOBS HOLE BOOKSHOP

Jabez Corner, Route 3-A
Plymouth, Massachusetts 02360
No telephone

Owners Jim and Pat Baker keep a good selection of out-of-print books on New England, general fiction and nonfiction, the occult, travel, nature, and folklore.

THE THEOLOGICAL BOOK CENTER

99 Brattle Street
Cambridge, Massachusetts
02138
Tel: 617-354-4691

Stocks books on theology and religion, especially Anglican.

TEMPLE BAR

9 Boylston St.
Cambridge, Massachusetts
02138
Tel: 617-876-6025

Founded 10 years ago by Jim O'Neil, this store specializes in photography but also carries poetry, small press books, rare books. It also has prints, photographs, and lithographs. Occasionally issues a catalog. Says O'Neil: "I handle books I'm comfortable selling, only."

MANDRAKE

8 Story Street
Cambridge, Massachusetts
02138
Tel: 617-864-3088

Irwin Rosen, the owner of this store, is the epitome of the personal service bookseller. The store specializes in art, architecture, psychiatry, philosophy and fine arts.

W. D. HALL

99 Maple St.
East Longmeadow,
Massachusetts 01028
Tel: 617-525-3064

Stocks general old and out-of-print books, specializing in Americana. Lists issued.

THE OPEN CREEL

25 Breton St.
Palmer, Massachusetts 01069
413-283-3960

Specialist in out-of-print books on fishing. By appointment only.

229

MITCHELL'S BOOK CORNER

54 Main St.
Nantucket, Massachusetts 02554
Tel: 617-228-1080

A general bookstore but specializes in whaling and maritime lore. Everyone from Walter Cronkite to Princess Grace shops here. Catalog sent out each November.

PANGLOSS BOOKSHOP

1284 Massachusetts Avenue
Cambridge, Massachusetts
  02138
Tel: 617-354-4003

Located in Harvard Square, facing the university, this store carries used and out-of-print books in the humanities and social sciences. Catalogs issued. Browsing is encouraged.

MICHIGAN

ARNOLD'S OF MICHIGAN

511 South Union Street
Traverse City, Michigan 49684
Tel: 616-946-9212

Fine and rare books of British and American literature and history, children's illustrated books, books on Michigan and the old Northwest.

THE CELLAR BOOK SHOP

18090 Wyoming
Detroit, Michigan 48221
Tel: 313-861-1776

Used and out-of-print books in all languages on Southeast Asia, Pacific Islands, Australia, New Zealand, South Africa.

CURIOUS BOOK SHOP

307 E. Grand River
E. Lansing, Michigan 48823
Tel: 517-332-0112

Used science fiction, Michigiana, comics.

CENTICORE BOOKSHOPS, INC.

336 Maynard St.
Ann Arbor, Michigan 48108
Tel: 313-663-1812

45,000 books, consisting of hardbound and paperback, new, remaindered, and used. Also has an art gallery.

PISCES & CAPRICORN BOOKS

302 S. Berrien St.
Albion, Michigan 49224
Tel: 517-629-3267 or
    616-258-2972

Specialist in fine, scarce, and rare books concerning nature, boating, fishing, hunting, etc.

ARGOSY BOOK SHOP

1405 Robinson Road, S.E.
Grand Rapids, Michigan 49506
Tel: 616-454-0111

Used and out-of-print movie material, nostalgia, science fiction.

WOODEN SPOON BOOKS

200 N. 4th
Ann Arbor, Michigan 48103
Tel: 313-769-4775

Used, rare, and out-of-print science fiction, Americana, American history, Civil War, and books about Lincoln.

HEDY'S BOOK & GIFT SHOP

20780 Mack Avenue
Grosse Pointe Woods, Michigan
    48236
Tel: 312-882-3566

Located in an exclusive suburb. A good general store with a religious emphasis. Owned by R. Eleanor Hedman.

PAIDEIA BOOKS

313 South State St.
Ann Arbor, Michigan 48108
Tel: 313-995-5200

Carries a quality selection of new, used, and out-of-print books on history, classical and medieval studies, philosophy, and religious thought.

MINNESOTA

THE EPISTEMOLOGIST

1010 SE 4th Street
Minneapolis, Minnesota 55414
Tel: 612-378-0534

Scholarly used, scarce, and out-of-print books about psychology, psychiatry, philosophy of mind.

MISSOURI

THE LIBRARY, LTD.

7538 Forsyth Blvd.
Clayton, Missouri 63105
Tel: 314-721-0378

New Downtown Branch

310 North Eighth Street
St. Louis, Missouri 63101
Tel: 314-241-6880

Good general bookstore offering "the ultimate in service" and specializing in children's books, psychology, and hardback fiction. Super Christmas catalog has been featured in Publishers Weekly. *Owners are Mr. and Mrs. Alan Mittleman.*

BENNETT SCHNEIDER

300 Ward Parkway
Kansas City, Missouri 64112
Tel: 816-531-8484

Located on Kansas City's famous Country Club Plaza, this is an old, reliable, and excellently stocked store.

PAUL'S BOOKS

6991 Delmar Blvd.
University City, Missouri 63130
Tel: 314-721-4743

"Best bookstore within 300 miles." Specializes in literary, children's, poetry, social sciences. Howard Nemerov and William Gass are regular customers. Intellectual center for the community. Owners Suzanne and Paul Schoomer say, "We've raised our children in the store." Sarah who is four and Ivan, age two, had a playpen right in the store.

LEFT BANK BOOKSTORE

399 N. Euclid
St. Louis, Missouri 63108
Tel: 314-367-6731

Located near Washington University, this store is run as a collective and gives a 10% discount on textbooks. It has a general collection of books, with a radical slant.

BIBLIOMANIA, INC.

#8 Westport Square
Kansas City, Missouri 64111
Tel: 816-756-1138

An amiable bookstore on three levels in Kansas City's lively Westport area. Recently remodeled, Bibliomania offers numerous enticements for book lovers:

comfortable chairs and space for browsing, wine and cheese parties for visiting authors, evening hours, and the personal attention of its knowledgeable staff. Diversified stock, good children's selections, strong periodicals section. Owned by Phillip M. May.

MONTANA

PHILLIP'S BOOK STORE, INC.

111 E. Main St.
Bozeman, Montana 59715
Tel: 406-587-3195

Founded in 1897, this is one of Bozeman's oldest enterprises and has served as bookseller to miners, cattle-drivers, and townspeople over the years. Carries general books, hardbound and paperbacks, with an emphasis on the West, travel, and art.

NEBRASKA

VILLAGE BOOK SHOP

8701 Countryside Plaza
Omaha, Nebraska 68114
Tel: 402-391-0100

When this store was founded in 1964, it was the first new bookstore in Omaha in 30 years. It carries hardbound and paperback books and stationery products.

NEW HAMPSHIRE

J & J HANRAHAN, INC.

62 Marcy Street
Portsmouth, New Hampshire 03801

Tel: 603-436-6234

Fine, antiquarian books on New England and early printed books.

NEW JERSEY

HAMMER BOOK COMPANY

308 Hillside Avenue
Livingston, New Jersey 07039
No telephone

Used and out-of-print specialists in Hebraica, Judaica, bibles, and chemistry.

PATTERSON SMITH

23 Prospect Terrace
Montclair, New Jersey 07042
Tel: 201-744-3291

Carries scarce and rare books and pamphlets on criminology and social problems, such as alcohol and narcotics, capital punishment, counterfeiting, suicide, frauds, and swindles.

PRINCETON BOOK MART

11 Palmer Square W.
Princeton, New Jersey 08540
Tel: 609-924-1730

Established in 1936, this store is an excellent alternative to the university bookstore. Owner Ralph Shadowvitz keeps the store well stocked in new hardbound and paperback books. Also carries remainders.

OLD BOOK SHOP

75 Spring Street
Morristown, New Jersey 07960
Tel: 201-538-1210

Carries a large selection of scarce, used, and out-of-print books of all kinds.

NEW MEXICO

ABACUS OF SANTA FE

652 Canyon Road
Santa Fe, New Mexico 87501
Tel: 505-983-2424

Specialist in used and out-of-print Southwestern Americana, pre-Columbian art and archaeology, Spanish and bilingual books.

TAOS BOOK SHOP

E. Kit Carson Road
Taos, New Mexico 87571
Tel: 505-758-3733

Located in a 150-year-old adobe building, this store caters to the art and intellectual community of the town. It has a good collection of books on the American Indian.

NEW YORK

AGNES ALBERTS BOOKS

67 Shoreview Drive
Yonkers, New York 10710
No telephone

Antiquarian books on theater, literature; specialists in Rudyard Kipling.

ACADEMIE BOOK GALLERY

1370 Lexington Avenue
New York, New York 10028
Tel: 212-348-0060

All kinds of out-of-print books on the American Indian, anthropology, military history, psychology, philosophy—fine illustrated classics.

AMERICANA BOOKS & GALLERY

36 Oak Avenue
Tuckahoe, New York 10707
Tel: 914-793-3199

Specialists in used and out-of-print books on military, aviation, medals, hunting, cavalry, etc.

THE BOOK CHEST

19 Oxford Place
Rockville Center, New York 11570
Tel: 516-766-6105

Old books on natural history, botany, zoology, ornithology, and similar subjects. Catalogs issued.

BOOKS AND COMPANY

939 Madison Avenue
New York, New York 10021
Tel: 212-737-1450

Just opened. Books still going onto the shelves. Very unusual beautiful store with signed first editions, wood shelves, brick walls, and panelled windows. Like a warm, comfortable, old English store. Distinctively Britain.

BUFFALO BOOK STUDIO

1441 Hertel Avenue
Buffalo, New York 14216
Tel: 716-838-5150

Old, rare, and out-of-print books, specializing in chess and checker literature. Ronald L. Cozzi, owner.

ARGOSY BOOK STORE

116 East 59th St.
New York, New York 10022
Tel: 212-PL3-4455

One of the largest and best-stocked stores of used, rare, and out-of-print books in New York City. Specialists in Americana, first editions, medical books, old prints, and maps.

CARAVAN-MARITIME BOOKS

8706 168th Place
Jamaica, New York 11432
Tel: 212-526-1380

Specialists in rare and out-of-print books of the sea and ships, including naval history, navigation, oceanography, piracy, yachting, whaling, etc.

THE CAT BOOK CENTER

Box 112 - Wykagyl Station
New Rochelle, New York 10804
Tel: 914-235-2698

Books on cats in English, French, and German.

FREDERICK N. ARONE

377 Ashforde Avenue
Dobbs Ferry, New York 10522
Tel: 914-OW3-1832

One of the country's leading used and out-of-print collections of anything to do with railroading, trains, and transportation, including books, timetables, advertising items, booklets, brochures, etc.

CARNEGIE BOOK SHOP

140 East 59th Street
New York, New York 10022
Tel: 212-PL5-4861 and 62

An enormous stock of used, rare, out-of-print, and fine books on every subject. Catalogs issued.

SOHO BOOKS

307 W. Broadway
New York, New York 10012
Tel: 212-925-4948

Located in a former wine warehouse, this store is fast becoming a community institution serving New York's Bohemian section. Strong emphasis on arts, crafts, literature, poetry, occult.

PHILIP C. DUSCHNES

699 Madison Avenue
New York, New York 10021
Tel: 212-838-2635

Mostly rare books and first editions. Catalogs issued.

NYU BOOK CENTER

18 Washington Place
New York, New York 10003
Tel: 212-598-2260

Jo-Ann McGreevy, the manager, is one of the leading college booksellers. She operates her store not only for the students of the university but for the Greenwich Village community as well. Two floors, free lockers, a splendid supply of books.

DOBBS FERRY BOOK STORE

74 Main St.
Dobbs Ferry, New York 10522
Tel: 914-478-2127

Used and out-of-print books of modern literature, detective, and Western fiction.

HOUSE OF BOOKS, LTD.

667 Madison Avenue
New York, New York 10021
Tel: 212-PL5-5998

Used and rare 20th-century first editions. Catalogs issued.

CINEMABILIA

10 West 13th St.
New York, New York 10011
Tel: 212-989-8519

One of the world's largest new and used film bookshops. Also carries stills, posters, and other ephemera.

TOTTERIDGE BOOK SHOP

667 Madison Avenue
New York, New York 10021
Tel: 212-421-1040

Carries mostly rare books, including first editions.

GRANT'S BOOK SHOP

255 Genessee St.
Utica, New York 13501
Tel: 315-724-4156

In operation for over a century, this store specializes in new and used rare and out-of-print books concerning upstate New York, the Mohawk Valley, and Americana.

XIMENES

120 East 85th St.
New York, New York 10028
Tel: 212-744-0226

The shop stocks rare and fine books of early English fiction and literature; also early American literature.

THE HENNESSEYS

4th and Woodlawn
Saratoga Springs, New York 12866
Tel: 518-584-4921

Out-of-print books on Americana, art, history, literature, and sports.

MCDONALD'S BOOK ENDS

125 Water St.
Catskill, New York 12414
Tel: 518-943-3520

Used and out-of-print books on the Catskill Mountains and upstate New York.

THE GOOD TIMES

150 East Main Street
Port Jefferson, New York 11777
Tel: 516-928-2664

Out-of-print and used hardcover and paperbounds, specializing in literary, social, and labor movement histories.

MADISON AVENUE BOOKSHOP

833 Madison Avenue
New York, New York 10021
Tel: 212-535-6130

You might spot Jacqueline Onassis shopping in this store: she's a frequent customer. Located in the blue-chip section of Manhattan's Upper East Side, this general store is managed by Rodney Pelter, one of the leading bookmen in New York. The store is one of the best service bookstores in the entire country.

238

ANDREW WITTENBORN

152 Mountain Road
Pleasantville, New York 10570
Tel: 914-769-9018

*Dealer in books on the au-
tomobile.*

SEVEN GABLES BOOKSHOP

3 West 46th St.
New York, New York 10036
Tel: 212-575-9257

*Out-of-print American juveniles,
poetry, fiction, and drama of the
19th century.*

MAPLETON HOUSE BOOKS,
INC.

112 Crown Street
Brooklyn, New York 11225
Tel: 212-772-8170

*Books on dentistry, plastic and
cosmetic surgery, arthritis,
headaches, and related subjects.*

RODGERS BOOK BARN

Hillsdale, New York 12529
Tel: 518-325-3610

*Stocks a large selection of gen-
eral used books with a heavy emphasis in literature, theater, and
feminism.*

E. S. WILENTZ'S
EIGHTH STREET BOOKSHOP

17 West 8th St.
New York, New York 10011
Tel: 212-254-3210

*Certainly the best bookstore in
Greenwich Village, the 8th St.
Bookshop is one of the best in the
city. Three full floors of hundreds of thousands of new books.
Superb paperback collection of
poetry, drama, film, fiction, art,
history, politics.*

NASERALISHAH BOOKSHOP

240 West 72nd St.
New York, New York 10023
Tel: 212-873-0670

*A general bookstore carrying
hard and paper books, the
Naseralishah (formerly Radius
Books) has one of the best collections of spiritual books in the
country. Prints, cards, posters,
and original prints are also sold
here. Classical music on the hi-fi
and a constantly perking coffeepot make the store pleasant to
browse in. Occasional films, autographings, poetry readings.*

THE VILLAGE GREEN
  BOOKSTORE

766 Monroe Avenue
Rochester, New York 14607
Tel: 716-461-5380

New and used paperbacks of science fiction, poetry, mysteries, literature, art, and hardbacks of art books, photography, poetry, and science fiction.

ELYSIAN FIELDS
  BOOKSELLERS

81-13 AB Broadway
Elmhurst, New York 11373
Tel: 212-473-2661

Specialists in homosexuality in literature and gay life in literature and history. Catalogs issued.

THE BIBLIOPHILE

148 West 72nd St.
New York, New York 10023
Tel: 212-873-2364

A new general bookstore that is spacious and bright and caters to the many actors and actresses who live on the Upper West Side, by way of an excellent collection of theater books, individual plays, and film books, both hardbound and paper.

HARCOURT BRACE AND
JOVANOVICH BOOKSTORE

757 Third Avenue
New York, New York 10017
Tel: 212-888-3333

A splendid selection of paperback and hardcover books. Several nooks and crannies to get lost in make this shop an interesting one. A good place to pick up a best seller the day it comes out—or even the day before.

NORTH CAROLINA

GRANDPA'S HOUSE

Highway 27 West
Troy, North Carolina 27371
Tel: 919-572-3484

Located in beautiful Montgomery County, this store carries old, scarce, and out-of-print books of all kinds.

INTIMATE BOOKSHOP #1

119 E. Franklin St.
Chapel Hill, North Carolina
27514
Tel: 919-929-0411

This store has been known for its large general stock and fine personal service since the 1930s. Its sister store, in Charlotte, also carries original graphics.

STEVENS BOOK SHOP

Corner of North and Main
Streets
Wake Forest, North Carolina
27587
Tel: 919-556-3830

New and used books specializing in biography, church history, religion and theology, biblical studies. Lists issued.

NORTH DAKOTA

ROOM FOR READING

15 N. Third St.
Grand Forks, North Dakota
58201
Tel: 701-772-9112

This store started out in a tiny basement as the first general full-service bookstore in Grand Forks. Now it is one of the city's major businesses. It contains a large stock of quality books and is well known throughout North Dakota as one of the best places to buy books.

OHIO

THE BOOKSELLER, INC.

521 West Exchange Street
Akron, Ohio 44302
Tel: 216-762-3101

Well-organized general stock of quality used and out-of-print books and magazines, specializing in Ohioana, U.S. Army aviation, and juveniles. Catalogs issued.

BURROWS

419 Euclid Avenue
Cleveland, Ohio 44114
Tel: 216-861-1400, ext. 282

Clevelanders love to browse this store because of its large, varied stock of new hardbound and paperback books. This is one of four branches in the Midwest.

241

PUBLIX BOOK MART

1310 Huron Road
Cleveland, Ohio 44115
Tel: 216-621-6624

In operation since 1937, this store carries over 100,000 books of all kinds. The citizens of Cleveland protested so passionately against the store's going out of business recently that the owners decided to keep it going.

GILDENMEISTER BOOK SHOP

13212 Shaker Square
Cleveland, Ohio 44120
Tel: 216-752-9150

A brand-new store with a full line of books. Double-level quarters. Richard Gildenmeister, the owner and manager, was formerly the buyer and manager of Higbee's Burrows' book departments.

OKLAHOMA

LEWIS MEYER BOOK STORE, INC.

3401 S. Peoria St.
Tulsa, Oklahoma 74105
Tel: 918-742-5821

Good general bookstore. Host of one of the oldest book review shows in the United States. Owner Meyer is author of three books, including two novels, one of them, The Customer is Always, *about his life with the store.*

AVONDALE BOOKSTORE

6459 Avondale Drive
Oklahoma City, Oklahoma 73116
Tel: 405-848-2697

A fine general bookstore that carries hardbound, paperback, and remainder books. Managed by Jane White and Bernice Butkin.

MARVIN MARCHER, BOOK-SELLER

6204 N. Vermont
Oklahoma City, Oklahoma 73112
Tel: 405-946-6270

Complete stock of books on firearms, hunting, fishing, weaponry, etc.

OREGON

AUTHORS OF THE WEST

191 Dogwood Drive
Dundee, Oregon 97115
Tel: 503-538-8132

Specialists in used, rare, and out-of-print distinguished Western American literature. Located 20 miles southwest of Portland. By appointment only.

J. K. GILL, LTD.

2725 N.W. Industrial Street
Portland, Oregon 97210
Tel: 503-226-4611

A chain of fine bookstores (5 in Portland, 19 others in Washington, Oregon, and California), which is over 100 years old. Sells
books, office supplies, arts and crafts, games, calculators, even Chinese ware from the People's Republic of China.

BRIAN THOMAS BOOKS, INC.

921 S.W. Morrison
Portland, Oregon 97205
Tel: 503-222-2934

Owner Charles M. Gallaher stocks this store with over 50,000 volumes consisting of hardbound and paperback books, remainders, games, maps, periodicals, and prints. Good selections of fiction, psychology, arts and crafts, cooking, nutrition, and philosophy.

PENNSYLVANIA

APOLLO BOOK SERVICE

68 East Broad Street
Bethlehem, Pennsylvania 18018
Tel: 215-868-3674

Used and out-of-print American and English literature.

SANFORD BOOKS

King of Prussia, Pennsylvania 19406
Tel: 215-265-5075

An excellent general store with upwards of 20,000 volumes.

G. H. ARROW COMPANY

4th and Brown Streets
Philadelphia, Pennsylvania
19123
Tel: 215-WA2-3211

Old periodicals in all fields of science, medicine, liberal arts, and learned societies.

SESSLER'S BOOKSHOP

1308 Walnut St.
Philadelphia, Pennsylvania
19107
Tel: 215-735-1086

Featuring new editions, Sessler's also carries antiquarian books.

LEHIGH UNIVERSITY BOOKSTORE

Maginnes Hall
Bethlehem, Pennsylvania 18015
Tel: 215-691-7000

Established in 1855. This is an excellent, large college bookstore.

UNIVERSITY OF PITTSBURGH BOOK CENTER

4000 Fifth Avenue
Pittsburgh, Pennsylvania 15213
Tel: 412-624-4050

Directed by Mary Bonach, this is one of the best college bookstores in the country.

GETTYSBURG CHRISTIAN BOOKSTORE

24 Chambersburg Street
Gettysburg, Pennsylvania 17325
Tel: 717-334-8634

Used and scarce books on Pennsylvania.

FRIGATE BOOK SHOP, INC.

16 E. Highland Avenue
Philadelphia, Pennsylvania
19118
Tel: 215-248-1065

Located in the Chestnut Hill section, this is one of the best traditional and personal general bookstores in the area. Established over half a century ago. Owner and manager: Thomas Emmons.

THE TUCKERS

2236 Murray Avenue
Pittsburgh, Pennsylvania 15217
Tel: 412-521-0249

Out-of-print and scarce books of a general nature, with an emphasis on Pittsburgh and southwestern Pennsylvania.

GEORGE S. MACMANUS CO.

1317 Irving Street
Philadelphia, Pennsylvania
  19107
Tel: 215-735-4456

*Specialists in rare and scarce
books of Americana and literature.*

BETTY SCHMID

485 Sleepy Hollow Road
Pittsburgh, Pennsylvania 15228
Tel: 412-341-4597

*Stocks any kind of book, periodi-
cal, program, or photos concerning the circus.*

RAY RILING ARMS BOOKS CO.

6844 Gorsten St.
Philadelphia, Pennsylvania
  19119
Tel: 215-438-2456

*Stocks books on hunting, shoot-
ing, arms, armor, war, infantry,
cavalry, etc.*

RITTENHOUSE MEDICAL
  BOOK STORE

1706 Rittenhouse Square
Philadelphia, Pennsylvania
  19103
Tel: 412-545-6072 and
  412-545-4274

*Stocks all kinds of medical books
and books relating to medicine,
dentistry, and pharmacy.*

RHODE ISLAND

COLLEGE HILL BOOKSTORE

252 Thayer St.
Providence, Rhode Island 02906
Tel: 401-751-6404

*An excellent general store carry-
ing new hardbound and paperback books.*

BOOK & TACKLE SHOP

7 Bay St.
Westerly, Rhode Island 02891
Tel: 401-596-0700
Newton Tel. (Winter):
  617-965-0459

*Perhaps the only store in the
United States that takes a summer vacation and has two addresses. Owner Bernie Gordon
has his winter headquarters in
Newton, Massachusetts, and
moves the store's operation to
Rhode Island every summer. The
store carries used and general
books with a specialty in fishing.*

SOUTH CAROLINA

BOOK BASEMENT, INC.

241 King Street
Charleston, South Carolina
  29401
Tel: 803-722-0690

Specialists in new and used books about South Carolina, North Carolina, Charleston.

SOUTH DAKOTA

COURTNEY'S BOOKS & THINGS

2119 S. Minnesota Avenue
Sioux Falls, South Dakota 57105
Tel: 605-338-1101

Founded by Dr. Courtney W. Anderson. Carries new hardbound and paperback books. One of several branches.

TENNESSEE

GATEWAY BOOKS, INC.

6305 Baum Drive
Knoxville, Tennessee 37919
Tel: 615-584-6141

General bookstore with a huge stock of hardbound and paperback books. Nine stores in Knoxville area; 65 stores overall. Owned by Robert Werner.

TEXAS

BOOKSELLER

9751 N. Central Expressway
Dallas, Texas 75231
Tel: 214-363-0671

This specialty bookstore, located in a residential area, has a unique selection of art, music, drama, dance, fiction, and social science.

**BOYD'S LOVELACE
BOOKSTORE**

911 Indiana Avenue
Wichita Falls, Texas 76301
Tel: 817-766-3309

An excellent general bookstore. Carries new hardbacks and paperbacks and a full selection of remainders. Good section on games; a special section on Texas.

COLLEEN'S BOOKS

6880 Telephone Road
Houston, Texas 77061
Tel: 713-641-1753

*Has 30,000 used books in stock,
specializing in Texas but containing titles in every field.*

UTAH

BOOKS OF YESTERDAY

36 West Center
Logan, Utah 84321
Tel: 801-753-3838

*Specialists in rare and used
books on Mormons and Western
America. Owners Tom and
Elizabeth Miller will provide a
search for difficult-to-find
books.*

DESERET BOOK CO.

44 E. South Temple
Salt Lake City, Utah 84110
Tel: 801-534-1515

*Established in 1866, this store is
known as the book center of
"inter-mountain West." Eight
branches. They carry 35,000 new
and remaindered hardbound and
paperback books.*

VERMONT

HAUNTED MANSION BOOK-
SHOP

Route 103
Cuttingsville, Vermont 05738
Tel: 802-492-3462

*A unique Victorian house with
two floors of used, old, and rare
books and maps, specializing in
Vermontiana.*

ROBERT A. LEIGHTNER

115 Dunder Road
Burlington, Vermont 05401
Tel: 802-863-5464

*Carries rare and out-of-print
books on music and musical in-
struments.*

VIRGINIA

THE BOOK PRESS

420 Prince George Street
Williamsburg, Virginia 23185
Tel: 804-229-1260

Old and rare books on Americana, printing; books about books, literature, horticulture; cookbooks.

RAM'S HEAD

Towers Shopping Center
Roanoke, Virginia 24015
Tel: 703-344-1237

Opened in 1964. A good general store of paperbacks and hardcovers. Owned by John E. Rosemond.

THE RICHMOND BOOK SHOP

808 W. Broad St.
Richmond, Virginia 23220
Tel: 804-644-9970

Specialist in books about Virginia and the Civil War.

BOOK RENAISSANCE

1131 North Irving Street
Arlington, Virginia 22201
Tel: 703-522-1505

Specialists in out-of-print books on 20th-century art, avant-garde movements, art history, architecture, photography, design, music, dance, film, foreign-language books. Catalogs and lists issued.

JO ANN REISLER

360 Glyndon St. N.E.
Vienna, Virginia 22180
Tel: 703-938-2967

Specialists in fine and unusual 19th- and 20th-century children's and illustrated books.

WASHINGTON

THE SHOREY BOOK STORES

110 Union St.
Seattle, Washington 98111
Tel: 206-MA4-0221

One of America's largest dealers in new, used, and rare books, with over 1 million books in stock. Complete catalog issued.

DAVID ISHII, BOOKSELLER

212 First Avenue South
Seattle, Washington 98104
Tel: 206-622-4719

*A general collection of used,
out-of-print and scarce books.
Also books of all kinds on the
Japanese, Chinese, and Filipino
in America.*

ROBERT W. MATILLA

115 S. Jackson St.
Seattle, Washington 98104
Tel: 206-622-9455

*Stocks books on Alaska, the Arc-
tic and Antarctic, and the Pacific
Northwest.*

WISCONSIN

ARABEST BOOK SHOP

W. 224 S. 6800 Guthrie Road
Big Bend, Wisconsin 53103
No telephone

*Out-of-print books on horses and
Scottish terriers.*

BLACKHAWK BOOKS

3504 Blackhawk Drive
Madison, Wisconsin 53705
No telephone

*Used, rare, and out-of-print
books on Lincoln, Grant,
Roosevelt, American political
history, Americana, Wisconsin.*

CANADA

BATTA BOOK STORE

710 The Queensway
Toronto, Ontario, Canada
    M8Y 1L3
Tel: 416-259-2618

*50,000 used books on Americana,
Canadiana, mystery, travel, fiction. Catalogs issued.*

CLASSIC SHOP

1430 Ste. Catherine St. W.
Montreal, Quebec, Canada
    H36 1R3
Tel: 514-866-8276

*One of 20 stores in a well-known
chain (including a store on New
York's Fifth Avenue) and one of
four on Ste. Catherine's Street,
specializing in Canadian books,
paperbacks and hardcovers, and
best-selling American fiction and
nonfiction.*

SOL SNIDERMAN

154 Coburg Street
Stratford, Ontario, Canada
 N5A 3E8
Tel: 519-273-1075

*Out-of-print books consisting of
modern first editions, poetry,
literary criticism, fine printing.*

DORA HOOD'S BOOK ROOM
LIMITED

34 Ross Street
Toronto, Ontario, Canada
 M5T 1Z9
Tel: 416-979-2129

*Specialists in new and out-of-
print books on or about Canada.*

J. PATRICK MCGAHERN BOOKS

763 Bank Street
Ottawa, Ontario, Canada
 K1S 3V3
Tel: 613-233-2215

*Carries used books on Canadiana
and the Arctic, also modern Irish
literature. Catalogs issued.*

POMONA BOOK EXCHANGE

Highway 52
Rockton, Ontario, Canada
 L0R 1X0

*Canada's specialist in horticul-
ture, agriculture, botany, food,
nature, and related subjects.*

PETER L. JACKSON BOOKS
 AND PRINTS

23 Castle Green Crescent
Weston, Ontario, Canada
 M9R 1N5
Tel: 416-249-4796

*Specializing in scarce and used
books on the military, uniforms,
battles, and campaigns. Catalogs
issued.*

Index

A

Abacus of Santa Fe, Santa Fe, N. Mex., 234

A. Buschke, New York, N.Y., 147–48

Academie Book Gallery, New York, N.Y., 235

Agnes Alberts Books, Yonkers, N.Y., 235

Albatross Book Store, The, San Francisco, Calif., 26–28

Alphabooks, Encino, Calif., 219

Americana Books & Gallery, Tuckahoe, N.Y., 235

Anderson's Book Shop, Larchmont, N.Y., 130–32

Andrew Wittenborn, Pleasantville, N.Y., 239

Apollo Book Service, Bethlehem, Pa., 243

Appalachiana, Bethesda, Md., 98–99

Arabest Book Shop, Big Bend, Wis., 249

Argosy Book Shop, Grand Rapids, Mich., 231

Argosy Book Store, New York, N.Y., 236

Arnold's of Michigan, Traverse City, Mich., 230

Asian Books, Cambridge, Mass., 104–05

Audubon Book Shop, Washington, D.C., 52–53

Authors of the West, Dundee, Oreg., 243

Avondale Bookstore, Oklahoma City, Okla., 242

B

Bakka, Toronto, Ontario, 210–11

Ballet Shop, The, New York, N.Y., 168–69

Banbury Book Shop, Woodland Hills, Calif., 223

Baptist Book Store, The (chain), 215

Barbara's Bookstore, Chicago, Ill., 77–78

Barnes and Noble, New York, N.Y., 165–68

Barry R. Levin, Los Angeles, Calif., 222

Basement Book Shop, New Orleans, La., 86–87

Batta Book Store, Toronto, Ontario, 249

Bayou Books, Gretna, La., 227

B. Dalton Bookseller (chain), 214–15

Bennett Schneider, Kansas City, Mo., 232

Betty Schmid, Pittsburgh, Pa., 245

Bibliomania, Inc., Kansas City, Mo., 233

Bibliophile, The, New York, N.Y., 240

Billiard Archives, San Pedro, Calif., 220

Birmingham Bookstore, The, Birmingham, Mich., 117–18

251

Blackhawk Books, Madison, Wis., 249

Bodhi Tree Bookstore, Los Angeles, Calif., 18–21

Book & Tackle Shop, Westerly, R.I., 245

Book Basement, Inc., Charleston, S.C., 246

Book Cellar, The, Brattleboro, Vt., 193–&½

Book Cellar, The, Brattleboro, Vt., 193–94

Book Chest, The, Rockville Center, N.Y., 235

Book Den, The, Santa Barbara, Calif., 30–31

Book Galleries Inc., Hilo, Hawaii, 72

Book Mark, The, Tucson, Ariz., 4

Book Nook, The, Tacoma, Wash., 200–01

Book Post, The, Duluth, Minn., 119–20

Book Press, The, Williamsburg, Va., 248

Book Renaissance, Arlington, Va., 248

Books and Company, New York, N.Y., 235

Bookseller, Dallas, Tex., 246

Bookseller, The, Coeur d'Alene, Idaho, 75

Bookseller, Inc., The, Akron, Ohio, 241

Book Shop, The, Boise, Idaho, 73–74

Books Inc., Houston, Tex., 188–89

Books of Yesterday, Logan, Utah, 247

Book Stacks, Inc., Burlington, Vt., 195

Bookstalls, New York, N.Y., 141–43

Book Store, Inc., The, Boston, Mass., 101–03

Book Store, Inc., The, Des Moines, Iowa, 80

Book Store of Naples, Naples, Fla., 225

Bookstore of Old Greenwich, The Old Greenwich, Conn., 46–48

Books Unlimited Co-op, Berkeley, Calif., 7–8

Boyd's Lovelace Bookstore, Wichita Falls, Tex., 246

Brattle Book Shop, The, Boston, Mass., 103–04

Brentano's, New York, N.Y., 156–62

Brentwood Bookshop, Los Angeles, Calif., 220

Brian Thomas Books, Inc., Portland, Oreg., 243

Brillig Works Book Store, Boulder, Colo., 34–35

Brown Book Shop, Inc., Houston, Tex., 189–90

Buffalo Book Studio, Buffalo, N.Y., 235

Burrows, Cleveland, Ohio, 241

C

Cable's Book Store, Santa, Fe, N. Mex., 128

Caravan Book Store, Los Angeles, Calif., 220

Caravan-Maritime Books, Jamaica, N.Y., 236

Carnegie Book Shop, New York, N.Y., 236

Cat Book Center, The, New Rochelle, N.Y., 236

Cellar Book Shop, The, Detroit, Mich., 230

Centicore Bookshops, Inc., Ann Arbor, Mich., 230

Change of Hobbit, A, Los Angeles, Calif., 221

Charlotte St. Shop, The, St. Augustine, Fla., 224

Chatterton's, Los Angeles, Calif., 221

China Books, New York, N.Y., 132–34

Chinook Bookshop, The, Colorado Springs, Colo., 35–37

Cinemabilia, New York, N.Y., 237

City Lights Bookstore, San Francisco, Calif., 29–30

Classic Shop, Montreal, Quebec, 249

Cobble Court Bookshop, Litchfield, Conn., 41–42

Cody's Books, Berkeley, Calif., 10–12

Colleen's Books, Houston, Tex., 247

College Hill Store, Providence, R.I., 245

Courtney's Books & Things, Sioux Falls, S. Dak., 246

Coventry Books, Cleveland Heights, Ohio, 176–77

Curious Book Shop, E. Lansing, Mich., 230

D

Dartmouth Bookstore, Hanover, N.H., 126–27

David Ishii, Bookseller, Seattle, Wash., 249

Deseret Book Co., Salt Lake City, Utah, 247

Different Drummer Books, A, Burlington, Ontario, 205–06

Discount Books, Washington, D.C., 53–55

Dobbs Ferry Book Store, Dobbs Ferry, N.Y., 237

Dora Hood's Book Room Limited, Toronto, Ontario, 250

Downeast Book Service, Penobscot, Maine, 227

Drama Book Shop, The, New York, N.Y., 152–53

E

Edgecomb Book Barn, North Edgecomb, Maine, 227

Edward Andrews, Stamford, Conn., 224

Elysian Fields Booksellers, Elmhurst, N.Y., 240

Epistemologist, The, Minneapolis, Minn., 231

E. Shaver, Fine Books, Savannah, Ga., 226

E.S. Wilentz's Eighth Street Bookshop, New York, N.Y., 239

Everybody's, Los Angeles, Calif., 219

F

Fireplace Bookshop, Chico, Calif., 221

First Edition Bookstore, The, State College and Harrisburg, Pa., 182–83

Florence O. Wilson Bookstore, The, Wooster, Ohio, 178

Folio Books, Washington, D.C., 55–56

Foundry Bookstore, The, New Haven, Conn., 43–44
Frederick N. Arone, Dobbs Ferry, N.Y., 236
Frigate Book Shop, Inc., Philadelphia, Pa., 244

G

Gateway Books, Inc., Knoxville, Tenn., 246
Gaul's Book Store, Fort Lauderdale, Fla., 225
George S. MacManus Co., Philadelphia, Pa., 245
Gettysburg Christian Bookstore, Gettysburg, Pa., 244
G.H. Arrow Company, Philadelphia, Pa., 244
Gildenmeister Book Shop, Cleveland, Ohio, 242
Gnostica Bookstore, Minneapolis, Minn., 120–22
Goodspeed's, Boston, Mass., 228
Good Times, The, Port Jefferson, N.Y., 238
Gordon's Booksellers, Baltimore, Md., 228
Gotham Book Mart, The, New York, N.Y. 149–52
Grandpa's House, Troy, N.C., 240
Grant's Book Shop, Utica, N.Y., 238
Great Expectations, Evanston, Ill., 78
Greens Farms Bookstore, The, Westport, Conn., 49–50
Grolier Book Shop, Cambridge, Mass., 112–14
Guidon Books, Scottsdale, Ariz., 219

H

Hacker Art Books, New York, N.Y., 154–56
Hammer Book Company, Livingston, N.J., 234
Harry W. Schwartz Book Shop, Milwaukee, Wis., 203–04
Harvard Book Stores, Cambridge, Mass., 110–12
Harvard Coop, Cambridge, Mass., 108–09
Harvey Dan Abrams Booksellers, Atlanta, Ga., 225
Haslam's, St. Petersburg, Fla., 68–69
Hatch's Bookstore, Englewood, Colo., 224
Haunted Book Shop, Mobile, Ala., 1
Haunted Mansion Bookshop,, Cuttingsville, Vt., 247
Harcourt Brace and Jovanovich Bookstore, New York, N.Y., 240
Hedy's Book & Gift Shop, Grosse Pointe Woods, Mich., 231
Hennesseys, The, Saratoga Springs, N.Y., 238
Heritage Bookshop, Los Angeles, Calif., 220
Hermitage Bookstore, Inc., Jackson, Tenn., 184–85
Hobs Hole Bookshop, Plymouth, Mass., 229
Holmes Book Company, The, Oakland, Calif., 221
Hound Dog Press Book Shop, Decatur, Ga., 226
House of Books, Ltd., New York, N.Y., 237

How-To-Do-It Book Shop, Philadelphia, Pa., 179–81
Hungry Mind Bookstore, St. Paul, Minn., 123
Hunter's Books, Beverly Hills, Calif., 12–14

I

Image and the Myth, The, Beverly Hills, Calif., 222
Intimate Bookshop #1, Chapel Hill, N.C., 241
Ives Book Store, Fort Meyers, Fla., 225

J

J & J Hanrahan, Inc., Portsmouth, N.H., 233
J.K. Gill, Ltd., Portland, Oreg., 243
Jo Ann Reisler, Vienna, Va., 248
John Gach Bookshop, The, Baltimore, Md., 96–97
John Howell Books, San Francisco, Calif., 222
J. Patrick McGahern Books, Ottawa, Ontario, 250
Junction Book Shop, Peoria, Ill., 226
June O'Shea Books, Los Angeles, Calif., 223

K

Kennebunk Book Port, Kennebunkport, Maine, 90–94
Kennedy's Bookshop, Evanston, Ill., 226
Kepler's Books and Magazines, Menlo Park, Calif., 21–23

Kisch Book Shop, Santa Barbara, Calif., 221
Kramer Books & Afterwords Café, Washington, D.C., 57–59
Kroch's and Brentano's (chain), 214

L

Lee Street Book Shop, Brunswick, Ga., 226
Left Bank Bookstore, St. Louis, Mo., 232
Lehigh University Bookstore, Bethlehem, Pa., 244
Lennie's Book Nook, Los Angeles, Calif., 222
Lewis Meyer Book Store, Inc., Tulsa, Okla., 242
Library, Ltd., The, Clayton, Mo., 232
Lighthouse Bookstore, Rye, N.Y., 171–72
Lion Bookshop, San Francisco, Calif., 222
Logos Bookstores (chain), 215–16
Longhouse Book Shop Ltd., Toronto, Ontario, 206–09

M

McDonald's Book Ends, Catskill, N.Y., 238
Madison Avenue Bookshop, New York, N.Y., 238
Magic Fishbone, The, Carmel, Calif., 14–15
Mandrake, Cambridge, Mass., 229
Maple Street Book Shop, New Orleans, La., 85–86
Mapleton House Books, Inc., Brooklyn, N.Y., 239

Market Bookshop, The, Falmouth, Mass., 114–16

Martin D. Gold, West Cornwall, Conn., 224

Marvin Marcher, Bookseller, Oklahoma City, Okla., 242

Mickler's Floridiana, Chuluota, Fla., 225

Middle Earth Books, Philadelphia, Pa., 181

Mitchell's Book Corner, Nantucket, Mass., 230

Moe's Books, Berkeley, Calif., 8–10

Montana Books, Inc., Seattle, Wash., 198–99

Murder, Ink., New York, N.Y., 134–35

Muses, The, Morgantown, N.C., 173–75

N

Naseralishah Bookshop, New York, N.Y., 239

Nebraska Bookstore, Lincoln, Nebr., 124–25

Needham Book Finders, Los Angeles, Calif., 223

Nevin E. Lyon, North Hollywood, Calif., 223

New Canaan Book Shop, New Canaan, Conn., 42–43

NYU Book Center, New York, N.Y., 237

O

Oak Street Book Shop, Chicago, Ill., 226

Odyssey, South Hadley, Mass., 228

Old Book Shop, Miami, Fla., 225

Old Book Shop, Morristown, N.J., 234

Old Corner Book Store, Boston, Mass., 100–01

Old Harbor Books, Sitka, Alaska, 2–3

Old Louisville Books, Louisville, Ky., 227

Old Monterey Book Company, Monterey, Calif., 220

Old Printed Word, The, Kensington, Md., 228

Once Upon A Time, Montrose, Calif., 23–25

Open Creel, The, Palmer, Mass., 229

Owl and the Pussycat, The, Lexington, Ky., 82–84

Owl and the Turtle, Inc., The, Camden, Maine, 88–90

P

Page One, Columbia, Md., 99

Paideia Books, Ann Arbor, Mich., 231

Pangloss Bookshop, Cambridge, Mass., 230

Papa Bach, West Los Angeles, Calif., 221

Park Ridge Book Store, Park Ridge, Ill., 79

Patterson Smith, Montclair, N.J., 234

Paul's Books, University City, Mo., 232

Peninsula Book Shop, Palo Alto, Calif., 25–26

Peter L. Jackson Books and Prints, Weston, Ontario, 250

Philip C. Duschnes, New York, N.Y., 237

Phillip's Book Store, Inc., Bozeman, Mont., 233

Pickwick Books, Hollywood, Calif., 15–18

Pisces & Capricorn Books, Albion, Mich., 231

Plaza Books/Paper Vision, Santa Cruz, Calif., 31–32

Pomona Book Exchange, Rockton, Ontario, 250

Pooh Corner Book Store, Denver, Colo., 37

Princeton Book Mart, Princeton, N.J., 234

Publishers Bookshop, Inc., Little Rock, Ark., 5–6

Publix Book Mart, Cleveland, Ohio, 242

Q

Quinion Books, New York, N.Y., 143–44

R

Ralph Curtis Books, Hollywood, Fla., 225

Ram's Head, Roanoke, Va., 248

Ray Riling Arms Books Co., Philadelphia, Pa., 245

Reed Library of the Foot and Ankle, Des Moines, Iowa, 227

Remarkable Book Shop, Westport, Conn., 50–51

Richard Hansen, Auburn, Calif., 222

Richmond Book Shop, The, Richmond, Va., 248

Rich's, Atlanta, Ga., 70–71

Rittenhouse Medical Book Store, Philadelphia, Pa., 245

Rizzoli International Bookstore, New York, N.Y., 144–46

Robert A. Leightner, Burlington, Vt., 247

Robert W. Matilla, Seattle, Wash., 249

Rodgers Book Barn, Hillsdale, N.Y., 239

Room for Reading, Grand Forks, N. Dak., 241

Rose Tree Book and Antique Shop, Tombstone, Ariz., 219

S

Samuel Weiser's Oriental and Occult Books, New York, N.Y., 164–65

Sam Weller's Zion Book Store, Clearwater, Fla., 191–92

Sandy Book Store, Clearwater, Fla., 67–68

Sanford Books, King of Prussia, Pa., 243

Savile Bookshop, The, Washington, D.C., 60–62

Savran's Paperback Shop, Minneapolis, Minn., 122

Scene of the Crime, Sherman Oaks, Calif., 32–33

Schoenhof's, Cambridge, Mass., 106–07

Science Fantasy Bookstore, The, Cambridge, Mass., 105–06

Science Fiction Shop, The, New York, N.Y., 146–47

Scribner Book Store, The, New York, N.Y., 162–64

Second Story, Chappaqua, N.Y., 129–30

Sessler's Bookshop, Philadelphia, Pa., 244

Seven Gables Bookshop, New York, N.Y., 239

Shorey Book Stores, The, Seattle, Wash., 248

Shtetl, The, Los Angeles, Calif., 223

Soho Books, New York, N.Y., 236

Sol Sniderman, Stratford, Ontario, 250

Stevens Book Shop, Wake Forest, N.C., 241

Strand Bookstore, The, New York, N.Y., 136–39

Stuart Brent, Chicago, Ill., 76–77

Sun Dance Books, Hollywood, Calif., 223

T

Taos Book Shop, E. Kit Carson, N. Mex., 234

Taylors, Inc., Dallas, Tex., 186–87

Temple Bar, Cambridge, Mass., 229

Theological Book Center, The, Cambridge, Mass., 229

31st Street Bookstore, The Baltimore, Md., 95–96

This Old House Bookshop, Montclair, Calif., 223

Thunderbird Bookshop, Carmel, Calif., 220

Tillman Place Bookshop, San Francisco, Calif., 222

Totteridge Book Shop, New York, N.Y., 237

Treasure Chest Book Shop, Great Bend, Kans., 81

Tuckers, The, Pittsburg, Pa., 244

U

University Bookroom, Toronto, Ontario, 209–10

University Book Store, Seattle, Wash., 199–200

University of Pittsburgh Book Center, Pittsburgh, Pa., 244

U.S. Bookstores (chain), 216

V

Vermont Book Shop, The, Middlebury, Vt., 196–97

Village Book Shop, Omaha, Nebr., 233

Village Green Bookstore, The, Rochester, N.Y., 240

W

Waldenbooks (chain), 216–17

Walla Walla Book Shop, The, Walla Walla, Wash., 202

Walter E. Hallberg, Hartford, Conn., 224

W.D. Hall, East Longmeadow, Mass., 229

Weyhe Art Book, Inc., New York, N.Y., 169–70

Wyoming Bookshop, Cincinnati, Ohio, 176

Whitlock Farm Book Barn, Bethany, Conn., 38–41

Womanbooks, New York, N.Y., 139–40

Wooden Spoon Books, Ann Arbor, Mich., 231

Writers Bookshop, Denver, Colo., 224

X

Ximenes, New York, N.Y., 238

Y

Yale Co-op, New Haven, Conn., 45–46

Yes!, Washington, D.C., 62–66